THE WORLD
WITHIN
THE TIDE POOL

In the southern hemisphere where the oceans are uninterrupted by land, high tide looks very different: a single great bulge of water encircling the earth.

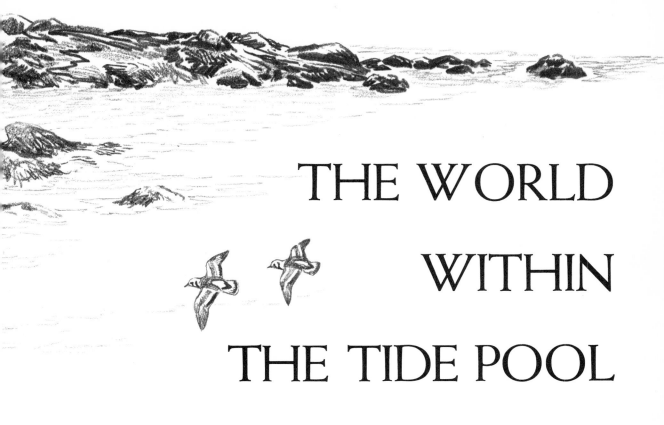

THE WORLD

WITHIN

THE TIDE POOL

by

Robert Silverberg

Illustrations by Bob Hines

WEYBRIGHT AND TALLEY
New York

THE WORLD WITHIN THE TIDE POOL

Book design by C. R. Bloodgood

Weybright and Talley
750 Third Avenue, New York, N.Y. 10017

LIBRARY OF CONGRESS CATALOG CARD NUMBER: 78-186560

MANUFACTURED IN THE UNITED STATES OF AMERICA

Contents

v

THE WORLD
WITHIN
THE TIDE POOL

The Shoreline Environment

THE tide is out, now. We can go down to the edge of the sea, along the sloping rocky breast of the shore. We enter an exposed world, a vulnerable world, a world out of its element, a world that holds its breath, waiting for the return of the lifegiving waters. Here, thick curtains of rubbery seaweed hang, limp and sagging, the heavy fronds moist and gleaming. In this flattened jungle huddle shoreline creatures caught above the tideline by the ebbing of the waters: crabs, a starfish or two, sea urchins, and others, keeping damp under the seaweed strands until the tide comes in again. Here, on these boulders higher above the water, we see the little white domes, clustered in hundreds or thousands, in which the barnacles live; each barnacle-house has its twin doors shut tight, to keep the moisture within. On the same rocks are incredible masses of dark musselshells, also clamped shut so that their occupants will not perish from the dryness in the hours of low tide. Here are snails, sealed snugly inside virtually airtight shells. Here are limpets and chitons and whelks

In the Littorina Zone the periwinkle, a kind of snail, dwells on rocks beyond the reach of the waves; needing more water, barnacles and mussels live closer to the sea in the Balanoid Zone; small fish can survive only in the Laminaria Zone which contains the widest variety of life forms.

and other inhabitants of the shoreline. Everything is suspended. Everything waits.

But as we pick our way cautiously through the exposed low-tide world, we find places where life goes on as usual, where the ebbing of the tide has made little or no difference to the small organisms that dwell there. These are the tide pools: miniature worlds, pocket universes, self-contained sanctuaries, in which we may see the whole complex life-cycle of the seashore environment acted out on a small scale.

To see tide pools one must go to a rockbound shore, not a sandy one. The world has more than a million miles of coastline—54,000 miles along the edges of the United States alone, counting all the inlets and crannies. But much of this is sandy shore. Sandy beaches are found where geological processes are causing the shoreline to rise, exposing large areas of sea bottom. The sea's floor is covered, just offshore, with a blanket of fine sand formed by the grinding down of rock through the ceaseless action of the waves; and so in regions of rising shoreline we have the long sandy beaches familiar to millions of Americans from Massachusetts to Florida.

Compared with a rocky shore, a sandy one seems a barren place. There is plenty of life, but nearly all of it is hidden life, burrowing out of sight in the sand. Clams and other shellfish, worms of many kinds, certain types of shrimps and snails, sand dollars, and any number of other creatures occupy the snug zone a few inches below the surface. Obtaining moisture is never a problem there, since the sand retains the water that sweeps over the beach at high tide. Those organisms that need frequent contact with the air can have it by extending a tube to the surface, by constructing air-passages leading to their dens, or by cautiously coming up through the sand from time to time. The human visitor, though, sees very little of this underground population. Tiny openings in the sand, slight movements of the upper layers, a scattering of the shells of dead creatures, an occasional glimpse of a scuttling sand-crab—those are the usual rewards of one who hopes to encounter the life-forms of a sandy shore.

THE WORLD WITHIN THE TIDE POOL

It is very different on a rocky coast. Such coasts are found where the shoreline is gradually sinking, and the sea has been able to carve the land into cliffs, arches, terraces, caves, and boulders. Where the underlying stone at the sea's edge is sturdy enough to resist the constant pounding, a rough, irregular, rocky coastline forms. There is often some sand on a rocky beach, deposited by the crashing waves, but the stark and somber cliffs and boulders that rise above the churning water dominate the scene. Much of the western coast of North America has this kind of shoreline, as does the eastern coast north of Cape Cod. Just above Boston one finds isolated rocky headlands at first, and then, from northern New England on through Newfoundland, an almost unbroken succession of granite cliffs and sloping rock-ribbed promontories faces the sea.

On such a coast a rich, fascinating, highly visible community of life-forms develops. A sandy shore is flat and open, and the grains of sand are forever being disturbed by the waves, so that the surface is yielding and unstable, offering no place for a foothold. But a rocky shore provides a variety of intricate shelters in which marine creatures can find niches. The offshore rocks become anchors for massive growths of seaweed, in the huge swaying fronds of which a host of small animals nestle and cling, hunting the even smaller creatures the waves bring them. Barnacles, mussels, and other permanently fixed forms attach themselves to the higher rocks. Snails, urchins, anemones, and starfish occupy the infinity of crevices and cracks.

This is the teeming world of the tidal strip—bounded at its lower end by the open sea and at the upper by the dry land. Between those extremes, in that ever-changing realm where the ebb and flow of the tides now submerge and now expose the land, dwell some of our planet's most remarkable creatures, designed by evolution to survive in a taxing environment that subjects them each day to constantly changing patterns of severe stress.

Scientists have identified three main life-zones in the tidal strip of a rocky shore, and we can readily detect them if we examine such a shore at a time when the tide is low. Farthest from the sea is the Littorina Zone, which takes its name from its most typical inhabitant—the common periwinkle, *Littorina littorea*, a kind of snail. This is a territory that the waves can reach only when the tides are at their highest or when some fierce storm stirs up the sea; most of the time the Littorina Zone stands above the water and its only moisture comes from the spray thrown up by the waves crashing below. Yet this is enough to support a substantial community of marine plants and animals. The Littorina Zone is brownish-black in color, for its rocks are covered by a thin, tightly clinging growth of dark-hued seaweed. Over these tough plants creep the periwinkles, which can stand exposure to the air more readily than any of the other tidal-strip creatures. Various other hardy snails are found in this zone, and also a rugged barnacle, *Chthamalus stellatus*, which fastens itself to the rocks in places so high that they are dry ninety percent of the time.

The Littorina Zone marks the boundary between the sea and the land: the zone of transition, where conditions are so hard that only the most durable of life-forms can maintain themselves. Below it, closer to the water, is the Balanoid Zone, named for the common acorn barnacle, *Balanus balanoides*. The sharp, stony, grayish-white cones of these animals form a pebbly coating spreading over vast stretches of the rock. Light-colored seaweeds grow among them, giving this zone a prevailingly yellowish color when viewed from a distance. The edible shellfish known as mussels, growing in clumps by the thousands, provide areas of darker tone in this level of the shore. Periwinkles, crabs, and other roving creatures of the uppermost zone are found down here as well. The Balanoid Zone is covered by water about half the time, so dryness is not as much of a problem as it is higher up; at low tide the barnacles and their neighbors simply shut themselves tight to await the coming, a few hours later, of the water that is necessary to their lives. The challenge in this zone comes not from the absence of water but from the tremendous force with which it arrives: this is the surf zone, where the waves land with their greatest impact, hitting the rocks with a shock that has been measured at up to 6000 pounds per square foot. The barnacles and mussels and other Balanoid Zone inhabitants are designed to stand up to this tremendous battering, but even they are most numerous in sheltered places where they need not absorb the full blow. The seaweeds of this zone, mercilessly tugged and hauled and flung about by the heaving of the surf, are sparse and stunted.

The lowest of the three tidal-strip regions is the Laminaria Zone, which derives its name and its characteristic light reddish-brown color from the great seaweeds known as kelps (Laminaria). The kelps are a family of large straplike water plants that grip rocks firmly and extend their long flat ribbons for many feet, forming tangled masses that sway and surge with the movements of the sea. They cannot tolerate much exposure to the air, and so the only part of the tidal strip in which they grow is the one closest to the sea itself, where they are fully covered by water eighty percent of the time, or more. Thus, just as the uppermost zone shades imperceptibly off into completely dry land, this one drops subtly into the sea, merging at its lower end with the realm of the eternally submerged. The Laminaria Zone is the seashore's most heavily populated region, for it is harassed neither by the dryness of the Littorina nor by the pounding surf of the Balanoid. Here the huge fronds of seaweed create an underwater forest inhabited by starfish, crabs of many sorts, urchins, sea anemones, worms, small fishes, such delicate creatures as hydroids and bryozoans, and a galaxy of others. When the tide goes out, and the kelp droops and sags in the air, most of these animals take shelter under the moist kelp ribbons, and see the period of exposure through in one way or another; only the fishes must take care to reach the sea before it is too late.

Life in any of the three intertidal zones has its hazards. The tides vary greatly from day to day, bringing special challenges. Some life-forms which must breathe air at least occasionally, drown when an unexpected strong tide comes rolling in; others, exposed to the air too long by an unusually low tide, dry out and die. Storms, lashing the sea, may rip loose such attached organisms as mussels or seaweeds or anemones, or may hurl water-loving lower-level dwellers into the dry Littorina Zone to perish. Nature's violence can smother an entire section of seashore in sand, or can throw boulders about with devastating effect on the creatures living on them. Beyond this there are the ordinary dangers of daily existence: the animals of the seacoast must eat, and their neighbors are food.

But there are calm pockets within this turbulent world where many of the shoreline perils are less menacing. These are the tide pools. They are found on every rocky shore— wherever there is a natural basin or crevice or hollow, wherever some stony ridge or tumbled heap of rocks lies in such a way that water is dammed in a tight-walled corner and kept from draining back into the sea. Tide pools are found in all three of the tidal-strip zones, but their basic nature is the same in each: they are places that retain enough water to sustain marine life at times when the rest of the zone about them is exposed to the air by the ebbing of the tide.

Some tide pools are veritable seas in themselves, twenty or thirty feet in diameter, three or four feet deep. Others can be crossed in a single step, and hold but a few inches of water. There are round tide pools and oval ones and crescent ones and some that are nothing more than long narrow water-filled gullies between two ridges of rock. There are tide pools in the high Littorina Zone that are refilled only occasionally, and come dangerously close to drying out between the peaks of the tide. There are tide pools in the low Laminaria Zone that are wholly submerged most of the time, like everything else around them, and take on true tide-pool existence only a few times a month. There are tide pools hidden in caves, where sunlight cannot reach; there are tide pools in the shore's exposed flats, open to the sun all the day long.

The range of variations is almost infinite. But tide pools, high or low, great or small, have one important thing in common. Each is the home of a community. Each has its little population of salt-water creatures: oysters and mussels, starfish and clams, hermit crabs and sea urchins, periwinkles and barnacles, the whole parade of coastline animals. They live in a natural aquarium of extraordinary beauty. Along the sides and bottom of the tide pool grow thick carpets of seaweed, green and brown and red, not only providing a lush "underbrush" in which small creatures can hide, but lending delicate color to the pool. Animals that look like plants—sponges, hydroids, sea squirts, sea anemones—also cluster on the floor and walls of the pool, adding their own splashes of pink and green and yellow, enhancing the pool's density and richness of color.

The tide pool's population is a fairly permanent one. Elsewhere along the shore, only the barnacles and mussels and anemones and other fixed animals hold the same places day after day. Such mobile creatures as periwinkles, crabs, urchins, and starfish wander as they please in search of food, and move up and down through the life-zones in obedience to the fluctuations of the tide. They may form a little group for a few hours, but when the tide goes out they scuttle to safety, scattering in many directions. In the tide pool, though, where there is always some water no matter how low the tide, there is no need to be a nomad. There, not only the fixed animals keep their places; the same crabs and urchins and starfish can usually be seen at any time, prowling the same territory. If a number of pools are connected by easy passageways, there may be a considerable interchange of population as organisms move from pool to pool; if not, they are content to stay where they are, for the return of the tide will bring them a fresh supply of food. As the waves sweep up over the tide pool, temporarily joining it once more to the sea, they carry the multitude of microscopic beings that the waiting inhabitants of the pool devour. Thus, the tide pool becomes a settled, balanced community, its occupants as familiar to one another as those of any small town.

Penetrating the secrets of that community may not always be easy. Frequently, one must scramble over jagged, slippery rocks to reach a good pool, making one's visit during the hour or two a day that the tide most fully reveals it.

Tide pools are not only a visual delight, they enable us to view life forms from each tidal zone interacting to form a cohesive community—a microcosm seashore life.

**THE
WORLD
WITHIN
THE
TIDE POOL**

When one gets there, one may find that the sun is at such an angle that the surface of the pool is mirror-bright, giving one a lovely view of blue sky and fleecy clouds instead of sea-creatures; then it is necessary to crawl to a position from which one can see through that gleaming surface. Even then there may be no immediate rewards. Most of the tide-pool animals are able to detect the motions of anything as large as a human being in the vicinity of their pool, and all activity ceases: in their alarm they slip into hiding-places, or become as motionless as flowers, until the danger seems to be past. So one must squat or lie or kneel patiently at the edge of the pool, as still as they, waiting for the moment when the life of the pool resumes.

When it does, however, the effect is magical. Since tide-pool dwellers are trapped in a relatively small space, one sees the intricate interplay of seashore life in a concentrated fashion unavailable anywhere else. A tiny shrimp, almost transparent, darts by and is snared by the stinging tentacles of an anemone. The doors of the barnacles' cones are open, and little feathery feet wave busily, preying on organisms too small for us to see. Periwinkles, gliding over the rocks, scrape away microscopic creatures with their rasping tongues. A small octopus peers cautiously from a low cave at one side of the pool. Gobies, little bottom-dwelling fish, rest just above the fronds of seaweed, and in sudden startling gulps seize unwary worms. A starfish is wrapped around a clamshell, using its suction cups to pry the shell apart to get at the tender morsel within. An oyster drill's tall pointed shell rises above a mussel; the drill, a kind of snail, is tirelessly cutting through the mussel's shell in search of a meal. A spiny sea urchin, grazing on seaweed, wiggles its wicked needles as clouds momentarily hide the sun. From rock to rock climbs a small green crab with surprisingly big front claws; abruptly one of the gobies is caught in a claw and the crab has his dinner. A bristly-looking worm crawls through a patch of sand on the pool's bottom, digging for hidden treats. A hundred dramas are playing at once—a hundred miniature tales of life and death.

The pools themselves—gemlike and shimmering—are a visual wonder apart from the doings of their inhabitants. Listen to the famed marine biologist Rachel Carson describing tide pools she often visited on the coast of Maine, in *The Edge of the Sea*:

"The pools have many moods. At night they hold the stars and reflect the light of the Milky Way as it flows across the sky above them. Other living stars come in from the sea: the shining emeralds of tiny phosphorescent diatoms—the glowing eyes of small fishes that swim at the surface of the dark water, their bodies slender as matchsticks, moving almost upright with little snouts uplifted—the elusive moonbeam flashes of comb jellies that have come in with a rising tide. Fishes and comb jellies hunt the black recesses of the rock basins, but like the tides they come and go, having no part in the permanent life of the pools.

"By day there are other moods. Some of the most beautiful pools lie high on the shore. Their beauty is the beauty of simple elements—color and form and reflection. I know one that is only a few inches deep, yet it holds all the depth of the sky within it, capturing and confining the reflected blue of far distances. The pool is outlined by a band of bright green, a growth of one of the seaweeds called *Enteromorpha*. The fronds of the weed are shaped like simple tubes or straws. On the land side a wall of gray rock rises above the surface to the height of a man, and reflected, descends its own depth into the water. Beyond and below the reflected cliff are those far reaches of the sky. When the light and one's mood are right, one can look down into the blue so far that one would hesitate to set foot in so bottomless a pool. Clouds drift across it and wind ripples scud over its surface, but little else moves there, and the pool belongs to the rock and the plants and the sky.

"In another high pool nearby, the green tube-weed rises from all of the floor. By some magic the pool transcends its realities of rock and water and plants, and out of these elements creates the illusion of another world. Looking into the pool, one sees no water but instead a pleasant landscape of hills and valleys with scattered forests. Yet the illusion is not so much that of an actual landscape as of a painting of one; like the strokes of a skillful artist's brush, the individual fronds of the algae do not literally portray trees, they merely suggest them. But the artistry of the pool, as of the painter, creates the image and the impression."

Because tide pools contain water under almost all circumstances, their inhabitants are not neatly graded and assorted in zones according to the length of time they can tolerate exposure to air, as are the life-forms that live on the open shore. Instead the pools contain a jumble of organisms from each of the zones of the tidal strip, intermingled in an almost random way. Of course, some zonation is seen even in the tide pools. The high pools of the Littorina Zone usually have only a handful of hardy species: some periwinkles and barnacles, some water-dwelling insects, the upper-zone seaweeds. One would not expect to find starfish or gobies up there. The low pools, those that are frequently engulfed by the sea, hold many creatures more commonly found in the sea itself: shrimp, sea urchins, fish, and the free-swimming, ocean-going young of barnacles and mussels. In the middle pools the mixture is greatest: here one has the usual creatures of the Littorina and Balanoid Zones, plus organisms normally found closer to the water, who have been swept up to this level on the breast of the high tide and who have been able to find permanent niches in a pool.

Although the tide-pool dwellers are exempt from the extremes of wetness and dryness that cause the open shore to be divided into life-zones, the pools themselves make such demands on their inhabitants that only the rugged are able to survive. On a summer day when the sun is shining, the temperature of a pool cut off from the sea by low tide often rises toward the danger level. If you put your finger into a tide pool at midday, the warmth of the water may surprise you; it may seem like the water of a warm bathtub. By early afternoon, the temperature in shallow pools and in those high on the shore (where they are infrequently replenished by cooler water from the sea) may be 100°F. or more; most of the animals will be in distress and some may have died.

It is lack of oxygen, as much as the heat, that causes this. Sunlight induces the seaweed in a tide pool to manufacture oxygen, but as temperature rises the oxygen rises, too, streams of bubbles climbing toward the surface and going off into the air. As the oxygen level drops, and it becomes more difficult to extract the remaining oxygen from the water, the gills of fish and other gilled creatures in the pool begin to move more rapidly. Some organisms go limp or close their shells to conserve energy, but gradual suffocation will be the fate of all if fresh supplies of water do not reach the pool soon. In the open sea, the beating of the waves continually mixes oxygen into the water, which is in constant circulation anyway; but in the closed system of a tide pool a hot summer day can make many creatures the victims of oxygen starvation.

Heat also causes the tide pool's water to evaporate; and though the total evaporation of the pool is rarely a danger except in very shallow pools far from the shoreline, a change in the pool's salt level is a serious matter. There is, on the average, about a quarter of a pound of salt in every gallon of seawater, although the sea is not equally salty everywhere. The water off Florida is saltier than the water off New Jersey; the Atlantic is saltier than the Pacific. The Red Sea and the Persian Gulf have water containing about forty parts of salt per thousand parts of water, but the Baltic Sea in northern Europe has only two to seven parts of salt per thousand. Variations in temperature and evaporation rates are responsible for these differences. Whatever the local concentration of salt may be, the marine animals of the region adapt to it and regard it as normal. It governs the balance of salt and water in their blood or body fluid. Any radical change in the ratio of salt to water in their immediate environment will upset this balance, with disastrous results.

In a tide pool exposed to strong sunlight, the water evaporates but the salt stays behind, and so a lengthy warm interval between one high tide and the next can greatly increase the amount of salt in the water. When the concentration of salt in the pool becomes very strong, the less salty fluid within the tide-pool creatures begins to seep from them, and many of them die. In such pools a white crust of crystal-ized salt may be visible around the edges; this is a certain sign that its inhabitants are in trouble.

Too little salt is equally troublesome. A heavy rain can fill a tide pool with fresh water, diluting the pool's salt content. If a tidal interchange does not take place soon, filling the pool once more with salty seawater, the animals of the pool will start to absorb the less salty water that surrounds them. It soaks into their tissues and inflates them, causing them to swell and die.

Thus, the mysterious and wondrous world within the tide pool is subjected to a wide variety of environmental stresses: the coming and going of the tides, changes in temperature and salt content, fluctuations in oxygen and carbon-dioxide levels, and much more. Yet calamities do not happen often. For all its perils, the tide pool is usually a tranquil, sheltered place, the innumerable inhabitants of which are well equipped to cope with the challenges of their changeable environment.

2

The Rhythms
of the
Tides

IF there were no tides there would be no tide pools, and indeed many other aspects of life on our planet would be considerably different. Those who live inland scarcely ever think about the tides, but to people living along the coast they are matters of great interest and sometimes of urgent importance.

The tides were probably of no special concern to the earliest major human civilizations, those that developed four to six thousand years ago in Egypt, Mesopotamia, China, and the Indus Valley in India. They were all river-centered cultures—founded on the banks of the Nile, the Tigris and Euphrates, the Huang Ho, and the Indus—and while the people of those lands may have dabbled in ocean-going commerce, they paid more heed to their rivers than to anything which might be happening along their shores. The flow of rivers fluctuates throughout the year, growing strongly when fed by spring floods, weakening in the heat of late summer, but rivers do not usually have perceptible tides.

When the lands bordering the Mediterranean Ocean became important centers of civilization about three thousand years ago, there was little or no increase in knowledge of the tides, for the Mediterranean is almost entirely land-enclosed and its tides are so gentle as to be virtually nonexistent. People in less civilized places, however, were well aware of the tides from early times. Those who lived on the shores of the Atlantic or Indian Oceans in particular must have realized long ago that the water came up farther on shore at certain times of day than others. Those who depended for their livelihoods on fishing would have grown to know the tides well, and would have discovered that the advance of the sea happened twice every day. In the morning the water would sweep inland up the shore as though it meant to engulf everything, but after a few hours the flow would be reversed, the sea draining back into itself so that by early afternoon men could walk far out into areas that not long before

16

had been submerged. Then, later in the afternoon, the water would begin to come back, extending its reach inland until it covered as much land as it had earlier; at that point the sea would start to retreat again. So it would go, day after day.

They would have observed, also, that this twice-daily cycle of invasions and retreats reached its twin peaks at different times each day. If a point of high water came at noon one day, it would arrive at 50 minutes past noon the next day, and at 100 minutes past noon the day after that. This 50-minute increase was not an exact one; sometimes the high tide came 48 minutes later than it had the day before, or 51 or 52 minutes later. But throughout the year the average was about 50 minutes later per day.

Eventually, perhaps, one of these ancient fishermen would see a connection between the changes in the tides and the movements of the moon. The moon, too, he would realize, rose into the sky 50 minutes later each day. Did that mean that the moon somehow brought the tides with it as it climbed the sky? And the force of the tides appeared to be linked to the moon's phases. The highest tides, those that pushed farthest onto the land, always seemed to happen when the moon was full or when the moon was new. In the other two quarters of the moon's cycle, when only a half-moon hung in the sky, the rise and fall of the tides was never as great. But the best explanation that primitive man could give for any of this was merely to say that the moon-god was also the god of the tides.

When warriors and explorers from tideless Mediterranean countries ventured into lands where the tides were strong, they often received unwelcome surprises. Alexander the Great, invading India in 325 B.C., came down the Indus River with a large shipborne army, and was dismayed and alarmed by the power of the Indian Ocean tides rushing into that river's mouth to buffet his moored ships. Julius Caesar, leading a naval attack on Britain in 55 B.C., had an even more unfortunate experience: he unknowingly brought his vessels to shore and anchored them when the tide was unusually strong, and when it went out the level of the water dropped twenty feet, leaving the Roman ships high and dry.

Faced with these phenomena, Greek and Roman navigators and geographers began to make careful studies of these oceanic upheavals. Pytheas, a Greek mariner who sailed to Britain and the North Sea late in the fourth century B.C., is said to be the first to have made systematic observations of the tides, and the first who linked their large fluctuations with the phases of the moon. Strabo, who lived in the first century B.C., dealt at length with the tides in his *Geography*. He described the way tides rush dramatically up the mouths of certain rivers, and discussed the effect known as *diurnal inequality*—the tendency of morning tides on successive days to resemble each other more closely than morning and afternoon tides of the same day. Pliny the Elder, author of the encyclopedic *Natural History* in the first century A.D., gave a correct explanation of how the sun and the moon govern the tides, and accurately related diurnal inequality to the positions of those heavenly bodies north or south of the equator.

A complete explanation of the tides, however, had to wait until the dawn of the modern age of science. The great German astronomer of the early seventeenth century, Johannes Kepler, made an important contribution when he guessed that the tides occur because the water of the oceans has a tendency to rise toward the sun and the moon, but he was unable to say why such a thing should happen. His equally great Italian contemporary, Galileo Galilei, suggested that the earth's two principal motions—its daily rotation on its axis and its yearly revolution around the sun—must cause the huge mass of oceanic water to slide back and forth over the land. This, too, was part of the story, but only a part. Not until 1687, when the British mathematician Isaac Newton drew the movements of the tides into his theory of universal gravitation, was real understanding of the tidal phenomena attained. For the tides are primarily the work of gravity's pull.

Newton was examining motion of many kinds, trying to determine one law that would account for all aspects of movement. Why does an apple fall down, not up, when it drops from a tree? Why do the planets continue to circle the sun, and not go flying off into space? Why do the tides encroach on the shore and drain away?

By means of ingenious geometrical arguments, Newton demonstrated that the planets are prisoners of gravity. As moving bodies, they would shoot off into the depths of space, except that the force known as gravity pulls them back. Kepler had had this notion earlier. The pull, he said, radiated from the center of things—from the sun. Kepler had imagined that the sun gives off a force that controls the movement of the planets. But Newton saw things more profoundly. Gravity, he reasoned, is no unique power of the sun. Gravity is a universal force. The planets are exerting a gravitational pull on the sun even while the sun is pulling on the planets. The earth keeps our feet on the ground with its gravitational pull, but each of us pulls the earth toward us at the same time. Everything in the universe, Newton declared, simultaneously exerts a gravitational attraction on everything else. But that attraction is governed by the size of the body doing the attracting and by the distance between one body and another. The earth's pull against your feet is much greater than your pull against the earth, and so you cannot leap into the air and pull the whole earth after you. The sun's pull on the earth is greater than the earth's pull on the sun, and so the sun controls the earth's motions, not the other way around. Newton summed all this up in his law of Universal Gravitation:

Every particle of matter in the universe attracts every other particle along the line joining them and with a force which is proportional to the product of their masses and inversely proportional to the square of the distance between them.

The tides, Newton showed, are caused by the gravitational pulls exerted by the sun and the moon against the earth. The sun, of course, is much the larger—almost 25 million times as massive as the moon—and so might be thought to have the greater effect, but distance as well as mass must be considered in the mathematics of Newtonian gravitation. The sun is 93 million miles from us, the moon only about 240,000 miles; therefore the moon, being so much closer, plays the major role in determining the movements of the tides.

As the earth turns, presenting first one hemisphere and then the other to the moon every 24 hours, the moon's gravitational pull constantly tugs at the earth. (The earth's pull constantly tugs at the moon, too, which is why the moon cannot wander off to some other part of the solar system.) The moon's pull is greater on the side of the earth facing it than the side that is facing away, but even at its strongest the pull is quite gentle: the gravitational attraction that the moon exerts on a pebble lying in the moonlight is only one ten-millionth as strong as the attraction that the earth itself exerts on that pebble. Since the moon's pull is so weak by comparison, it cannot lift that pebble and draw it toward itself, nor can it cause any visible distortion of the rigid materials of the earth's crust. But water is more easily affected by gravity than solid ground, and the moon's pull is strong enough to lift the waters of the ocean toward itself a short way.

Thus, a bulge of water builds up on the side of the earth directly under the moon. On the opposite side of the earth, where the moon's pull is weakest, a second bulge forms, as a result of the workings of centrifugal force, which operates against gravity and constantly attempts to make things fly off the surfaces of rotating bodies. These two bulges are the high tides. At right angles to them are the places on earth from which the water has been drawn to form the two piled-up masses; in those places the tide is low.

With the earth making one complete turn on its axis every 24 hours, each area on the earth's surface could expect to experience two high tides a day—one when it is directly under the moon, one when it is facing away from the moon— and two low tides a day, when it is midway between the places where the water is piled up. If the earth were completely covered by water, this tidal cycle would be uniform and consistent everywhere, with two great tidal waves sweeping majestically round and round the globe at a constant height. But in fact seven huge continents interrupt the sweep of the two mighty tidal bulges and produce many local variations in the timing and height of the tide. Many other geographical factors also affect the tides, such as the contour of the coastline, the depth of the water, and the shape of the ocean floor. So tidal patterns vary widely in different parts of the earth. In open ocean the tide is normally two or three feet in height and arrives punctually twice each day; but only in the southern hemisphere, where the ocean forms a continuous band encircling the world, do the tides have the regularity they would have if ours were a planet of water. Elsewhere, the variations are quite striking.

In most places there are two high tides a day, coming, on the average, 12 hours and 25 minutes apart, and, as we have seen, the hour of high tide advances by about 50 minutes a day, keeping pace with the hour of moonrise. Around the Mississippi Delta and in the China Sea, though, high tide comes only once a day. On the Pacific coast of North America twice-daily high tides are found, but they tend to be irregularly spaced.

The range of the tide—that is, the difference in level between high and low water at any place—also varies tremendously throughout the world. In the Mediterranean the range never exceeds two feet. On the Florida Keys the range is equally narrow, but a little way up Florida's Atlantic coast the tidal range can get to be as much as 3 or 4 feet. Farther to the north, in the Sea Islands of Georgia, the range reaches 8 feet, though it drops to 6 at Charleston, South Carolina, and 3 at Beaufort, North Carolina. Nantucket Island, off Massachusetts, has scarcely any tide, although just 30 miles away on the shores of Cape Cod Bay the tidal range can reach 10 or 11 feet. Most of New England's rocky coast has a notably wide tidal range, particularly in Maine: 12 feet at Bar Harbor, 20 at Eastport, 22 at Calais.

Where certain unusual geographical circumstances prevail, tidal ranges far exceed these figures. The most spectacular tides are found where the inflowing water must enter a long, narrow channel, which bottles up the tide and lifts it to an extraordinary height. This phenomenon reaches its greatest extent in the Bay of Fundy, on Canada's eastern coast between Nova Scotia and New Brunswick. Twice each day some 100,000,000,000 tons of water rush in and out of this rocky channel, and the tidal range in some places is over 50 feet. At low tide, towering seaweed-encrusted cliffs stand fully exposed; then, with frightening speed and intensity, the water begins to enter the bay and fill it, temporarily drowning a vast expanse of what had only minutes before been accessible land.

Where the mouth of a river offers the proper geographical configuration, remarkable tidal effects also occur. A fierce wave known as a "tidal bore" rolls into the river from the sea twice each day with amazing impact. On the Tsientang River in China, high tide enters in the form of a bore that surges upriver as a wave 11 to 25 feet high, carrying 1,750,000 tons of water upstream a minute. The Chinese boatman take advantage of this, timing their upriver journeys so that the onrushing tidal bore sweeps them to their destinations. A tidal bore up to 16 feet in height regularly rushes 200 miles up the Amazon River at enormous speed, making a roar that can be heard for miles. In the Bay of Fundy, the tidal waters are funneled into the narrow neck of the Petitcodiac River near the town of Moncton, News Brunswick, creating a twice-daily wall of water that is only three to five feet high but which advances with impressive power and sound.

Tides vary in range not only from place to place but from time to time in the same place. As has already been noted, tides run highest at new moon and at full moon, and lowest when the moon is in one of its crescent phases. This is explained by the fact that the sun as well as the moon exerts a gravitational force affecting the tides.

When the moon is new, the moon and the sun are on the same side of the earth; when the moon is full, the earth lies directly between the sun and the moon. Either way, earth, moon, and sun are lined up in a straight row, and the gravitational pull of moon and sun upon the earth is combined. This causes a heightening of the tidal range. The high tide comes farther up on shore then than at any other time of the month; the low tide retreats farther, exposing more of the seabed. These exaggerated tides are known as "spring" tides, referring not to the season but to the way the water seems to spring up onto the land. For reasons that can only be made clear by complicated mathematics, spring tides occur a few days after the new moon and a few days after the full moon, rather than at the precise time of maximum gravitational pull.

During the first and third quarters of the lunar cycle, when only part of the moon's face is visible from earth, the sun and moon as seen from our planet are at right angles to each other. Each thus partly cancels out the gravitational pull of the other, and the range between high tide and low tide is at its smallest. These placid tides are known as "neap" tides

—from an old Scandinavian word meaning "scarcely touching" or "hardly enough." The difference between a high spring tide and a high neap tide may be only a matter of inches at a place where the tidal range is small, but it can be many feet where robust tides are experienced.

This ever-changing pattern of tides creates the three-zone structure of the rocky coast, and the all but imperceptible gradations of innumerable subzones within the three major zones. If we examine a headland on, say, the coast of Maine, we find that the highest ground of all lies always completely outside the ocean's reach; below it is a zone that catches a little ocean spray during severe storms; below that is a zone moistened by the spray kicked up by ordinary storms; another level down is a zone that receives spray when the high spring tide comes; next is the zone actually covered by the high spring tide. Beyond that we find zones that are covered by a high neap tide, by a low neap tide, by a low normal tide, and so on down to the lowest level of the shore, the region that remains submerged all the time except when the tide is at its feeblest ebb. Each of these zones has its characteristic color, its typical plant and animal population; though there is much overlapping of life-forms between one zone and the next, the population of the highest zone is almost totally different from that of the lowest.

And, of course, the fluctuations of the tides gives us the tide pools, those isolated pockets that remain filled with water even after the low tide has pulled the swirling, coursing waves well back from the rim of the land. When the tide is high, these pools are covered by water, often covered quite deeply; therefore if we would visit the tide pools, we must go down to the shore at a time when the tide is out and the intricate little worlds within the pools lie open to us on the bare shore.

Discovering the schedule that the tides keep in your particular area of the coast is generally not a very complicated project. Tide tables are often posted on beach bulletin boards in seaside resorts; sometimes they are published in

With the arrival of high tide a wall of water often five feet high will roar from the Bay of Fundy into the narrow mouth of the Petitcodiac River in New Brunswick.

daily newspapers, and they can be found in certain almanacs.
A tide table usually looks something like this:

| DATE | HIGH | | LOW | |
	TIME	HEIGHT	TIME	HEIGHT
Jul 1	11:16 AM	4.9 ft.	4:53 AM	—0.7 ft.
	11:29 PM	5.3 ft.	5:07 PM	—0.1 ft.
Jul 2	12:12 PM	5.0 ft.	5:43 AM	—0.5 ft.
			6:06 PM	0.1 ft.
Jul 3	12:25 AM	5.0 ft.	6:38 AM	—0.3 ft.
	1:05 PM	5.1 ft.	7:15 PM	0.3 ft.

From such a table—this is a real one, covering the tides near New York City one summer some years ago—we can get a good feel for the rhythms of the tidal cycle. We see, for example, that the morning low tide came exactly 50 minutes later on July 2 than on July 1, and 55 minutes later on July 3 than on July 2. We see that on July 1 the two high tides were 12 hours and 13 minutes apart, and that on July 3 they were 12 hours and 40 minutes apart. (There is only one high tide entry for July 2, the reason being that the full tidal cycle, averaging 24 hours 50 minutes or so, spans more than one full calendar day. The evening high tide on July 1 came near midnight; July 2's only high tide arrived shortly after noon; by the time the tide returned again, more than 12 hours later, the calendar date was July 3.)

The figures show us, also, that the range of the tide varies slightly from tide to tide and from day to day. The principle of diurnal inequality is at work here. All during the month of which the first three days are given here, the morning high tides are not as high as the afternoon high tides of the same day, and the morning low tides are lower than the afternoon low tides of the same day. The difference is sometimes quite pronounced; on July 23, the table reveals, the morning high tide reaches only 3.8 feet above normal, and the later high tide climbs to 5.0 feet. The transition from neap to spring tide and back would also be apparent if we had the full month's table before us: it shows the July 21-22 high tides of 3.7 feet as the lowest of the month, and the July 27 high tide of 5.9 feet as the highest.

For seekers of tide pools the table also holds important information. The best time to set out on a tide-pool trip is about half an hour before the point of lowest tide is reached; that way, the tide is retreating all through the first stages of your explorations. It is safe to stay for perhaps half an hour after the turn of the tide—that is, after the moment of lowest tide, when the flow reverses itself and starts to move toward the shore. On July 1, therefore, we would have to pay our morning visit to the tide pools well before breakfast, going out around 4:15 AM and staying until 5:15 or so. That day it would probably be best to make the journey in the afternoon, between 4:30 and 5:30 PM, since low tide is due at 5:07 PM. On July 2, the situation is not greatly changed; morning low tide is still extremely early, and afternoon low tide, coming at 6:06 PM, starts to encroach on dinnertime. On July 3 we get low tide at a more reasonable hour of the morning, but the late low tide will not come until 7:15, meaning that the tide-pool visitor would find himself still at the shore as night begins to fall—not a wise idea. Since the day's two low tides always must be spaced somewhat more than 12 hours apart, there will ordinarily be only one convenient opportunity a day to scout for tide pools. If that opportunity comes in midmorning, the next low tide will occur after dark; if there is a good tide-pool time in late afternoon, the next low tide will come before dawn.

Consulting the tide tables, then, is the simplest and most reliable way to plan your field trip to a tide pool. But it is not the only way. At most shore regions you can ask the local people—fishermen, preferably, if you can find any—when the low tides are due to come. Coastal dwellers almost always know. Or, best of all, you can calculate the rhythms of the tides yourself, if you will be spending several days at the same point along the shore. You need only watch the waves one day, and take note of the time when the seaweed-covered rocks stand most fully exposed. Low tide will come fifty minutes later on the following day, give or take a few minutes. If the tide pools are best revealed between one and two in the afternoon on Tuesday, you can expect them to be within your reach between two and three in the afternoon on Wednesday, between three and four in the afternoon on Thursday, and so on. As it was done in ancient times, so now you can use your powers of observation to compute the flow of the sea.

3

Animal Life
of the
Tide Pool

PASSIONATE botanists would certainly disagree with me, but the main attraction of the tide pool for me, and probably for most other visitors, is the wealth of animal life it contains. Elegant and interesting water plants abound in the pools, but it is the animals, engaged in the intricate network of life-and-death relationships that is their daily routine, who draw my attention most keenly.

Tide-pool animals are necessarily small ones. Many are microscopic or almost microscopic; most others, such as snails and barnacles, are no bigger than a fingertip. Crabs the size of one's fist are the giants of the tide pools, though in some regions one may find bigger creatures, an occasional octopus or lobster lurking in a sheltered nook.

The animals of a tide pool are usually harmless ones—to man, if not to each other. Sea anemones can sting, but only the tiniest creatures feel any effect. Crabs have wicked-looking pincers, but ordinarily no crab in its right mind would let a human being get close enough to it to be pinched. The shy octopus has a terrifying reputation in fiction, but not in fact. The only tide-pool dweller that offers any real perils to man is the spiny sea urchin found in warm climates; its long needle-like spines are fragile, breaking at the slightest touch and piercing the skin to cause painful infections and inflammations. But it is easy enough to leave these urchins alone if one finds them in a pool.

Tide-pool creatures are, almost without exception, members of that huge group of animals known as invertebrates—animals without backbones. This group includes all the relatively simple life-forms, beginning with one-celled animals, sponges, corals, and other uncomplicated organisms, and going up the ladder of evolution through the starfishes, worms, clams, and snails to such fairly advanced creatures as crabs, barnacles, and insects. It does not include the most complex forms of life: fishes, amphibians, reptiles, birds, and mammals. Fish, of course, are found in many tide pools, especially those closest to the sea where they are washed in and out of the pools as the tides change, but only by courtesy can they be considered regular members of the tide-pool community. Amphibians and reptiles are not found in tide pools; birds often come to prey on the little creatures of the pools, but they are not on that account to be thought of as tide-pool dwellers, any more than are the human beings who delight in peering into the pools. (And who, alas, too often "collect" their inhabitants.)

The tide-pool animals can be classified according to the way they obtain their food: there are those who hunt for it, those who graze, and those who sit eternally in the same place, waiting for their meals to come to them. Crabs are typical examples of the first class, periwinkles and limpets of the second, barnacles and mussels of the third. But all, in one way or another, must prey on other living things. Plants are capable of manufacturing their own food through the process known as *photosynthesis*, which makes use of sunlight and the green substance called chlorophyll to convert carbon dioxide, water, and minerals into edible carbohydrates, pro-

To resist the force of the waves the barnacle cements himself to a rock and extends feelers to catch food; when the water recedes his door plates clamp shut, trapping enough moisture for survival until the next tide allows him to feed again.

teins, and fats. Animals, though, having no way to carry on photosynthesis, are compelled to gather their food either by feeding on plants or on other animals.

Barnacles, who are often the tide pool's most numerous and conspicuous inhabitants, are masters of the science of sitting and waiting for their meals to come to them. They belong to the large group of animals known as the *crustaceans*, which includes lobsters, shrimps, crabs, crayfish, waterfleas, sand-hoppers, and many other creatures. Crustaceans are organisms of fairly complex structure, with jointed legs

31

and hard, horny skeletons that they wear on the outsides of their bodies. Most of them are quite active, crawling or hopping or swimming about, but the barnacle, alone in the group, remains fixed in one place throughout its entire adult existence.

A newborn barnacle looks very much like other newborn crustaceans. Eggs hatch in the parent's shell and grow into larvae called *nauplii*, which have three pairs of bristly legs, a pair of antennae at the end of each leg, and a single eye. Milky clouds of nauplii pour forth from the parent barnacles in incredible numbers and, carried off by the waves, swim into the sea. One zoologist studying barnacles on the Isle of Man, on the British coast, reported that a single barnacle produces about a thousand nauplii a year—and there were 1000 million barnacles living on a stretch of shore a little over half a mile long!

For about three months the nauplii swim near the surface of the offshore waters, nourished by big globes of fat. Gradually, as the fat is absorbed, they change form, developing a pair of shells, six pairs of swimming legs, and a pair of antennae tipped with suckers. The time is approaching when they must head for land. Floating with the tides, the young barnacles drift shoreward and look for a likely place to settle down for life. When they reach shore they may wander around for an hour or more, inspecting possible sites, searching for one that is not too smooth and slippery and that is not already occupied by certain microscopic plants that barnacles dislike. The ideal site for a barnacle seems to be one where other barnacles already are living—which is why great clusters of them accumulate along the coast. In the end, the barnacle may choose to settle on almost anything that provides a firm underpinning: a convenient rock, the hull of a boat or ship, driftwood, a sea wall, the pilings of a dock, even the shell of a mussel already inhabiting some cranny of the shore. The dwelling-place may be anywhere along the tidal strip, though usually it is in the upper half, in a region that is exposed to the air for long spans of time. Some species of barnacles favor the highest zone of all, where the sea comes

The unusual gooseneck barnacle is a seagoing creature: it prefers to attach itself to floating driftwood instead of the Balanoid rocks which form the typical habitat of its common cousin, the acorn barnacle.

only on the spring tides a few days a month, but most are found toward the middle of the tidal area.

When the barnacle has picked its place, it quickly cements itself head-down to the surface it has selected; so strong is the cement that the barnacle will never be in danger of being washed loose even by the heaviest waves. Now the outer shell begins to grow, and within twelve hours it is complete: a sharp cone-shaped one, looking something like a miniature volcano, with sloping sides and a "crater" at the summit. The shell consists of six closely fitted overlapping plates with an opening at the center that can be covered by two pairs of smaller plates.

Now the barnacle is set for the rest of its life, which may last three to five years if it is not scraped free by grinding winter ice, devoured by one of its natural enemies (certain fish, worms, and snails), or poisoned by a slick of oil dumped on the sea by the most dangerous animal of all—man. When the tide is low, it remains sealed within its shell, giving no sign of life. But as the water rises, bringing with it a horde of minute organisms, the barnacle's door-plates open and six pairs of delicate, feathery, bristle-covered feelers poke through. With these the barnacle hunts for its dinner, waving them in every direction, snaring the small organisms, pushing them into its shell to be eaten. When the water level begins to drop, the barnacle pulls in its feelers and shuts its door to await the next high tide. A sharp-eared observer who roams the shore at this time may be able to hear what one zoologist has called "the whispering talk" of the barnacles—the faint sound made as thousands of these creatures close their plates at once, "like shopkeepers putting up their shutters for the night." Sealed inside the shell with the barnacle is enough water to keep it alive until the sea rises again. Some barnacles near the high-tide line spend less than a twentieth of their lives under water.

There are many species of barnacles, although the differences between most of them can be detected only by an expert. The most common ones are the acorn barnacles, *Balanus balanoides*, which occupy the middle zone of the tidal strip. Higher on the shore dwells *Chthamalus fragilis*, which is distinguished by a brownish, leathery baseplate—something you can see only by prying the barnacle from its rock with a knife, thus killing it. And below the *balanoides'* zone lives *Balanus eburneus*, which has a stony white baseplate and is less tolerant of dry conditions than the other species. On the Pacific coast one sometimes sees an unusual type, the gooseneck barnacle (*Lepas fascicularis*), which, instead of fastening the base of its shell to a flat surface, grows at the end of a flexible stalk several inches long. Gooseneck barnacles usually attach themselves to driftwood floating in the open sea, but occasionally they may be seen along the shore.

The best place to watch barnacles in action is a tide pool, where the barnacles need not spend much of their time sealed up and the water is shallow and transparent. Hundreds or even thousands of the rough-edged stony shells may be crammed together in the pool. If one looks carefully when the sun is at the proper angle, one can see the tiny shadows of the barnacles' hunting-feelers flickering over the rocks in the pool. With the help of a magnifying glass, it is possible to see the slender feelers themselves, constantly sweeping in little organisms invisible to human eyes. But one must remain quite still while observing barnacles; though they are hidden upside down within sturdy shells, they have an uncanny way of knowing when intruders are about, and when a curious finger approaches a barnacle the small crustacean will slam its door-plates closed.

Areas not covered by thick masses of barnacles are likely to be blanketed by even greater quantities of another permanently settled inhabitant of the rocky shore: the mussel. Mussels are members of the group called the *mollusks*, which includes oysters, clams, snails, scallops, octopuses, squids, and many other creatures. The name of the group comes from a Latin word meaning "soft," for mollusks are soft-bodied, boneless animals, though most of them are protected by a hard shell. Mollusks such as mussels, clams, and oysters have two shelves or "valves," upper and lower, and so are known as "bivalves." Snails, having only one shell, are "univalves."

Like barnacles—with which they have little else in common—mussels begin their lives as free-swimming forms. During spring and summer the parent mussels shed eggs and sperm cells into the water, where fertilization takes place and larvae develop. One female mussel may release as many as 25 million eggs in a single spawning. Though only a fraction of these are fertilized, the numbers of larvae that result are hard to imagine; one patch of water no more than a yard square may hold hundreds of thousands of them.

The larva, shaped something like a top and equipped with a thin shell, reaches its full development in about a week and a half. Now it is long and flat, has the double shell of an adult mussel, and has grown a rubbery tube-shaped foot. Washed by the waves into the low-tide zone along the shore, the young mussel creeps about, using its foot to explore its

35

surroundings. On a sandy or muddy shore, the mussel looks for a solid surface—a jetty or breakwater, pilings, rocks, perhaps the shell of an oyster or clam. On a rocky shore its task is much easier, since footholds abound everywhere. It may nestle into the clump of thick root-like strands at the base of one of the big seaweeds, or it may select a rock. Instead of cementing itself to its resting-place as barnacles do, the mussel puts out anchor lines. A gland in its foot produces thin strands of a fluid known as *byssus*, which hardens upon contact with sea water; thus, the mussel fastens itself down with a series of tough glossy yellowish threads reaching in every direction. These threads secure the mussel against all but the most powerful surges of the sea, and if some of them are broken during a storm the mussel can spin new ones.

Immense quantities of the elongated blue-black mussel shells pile up in small areas. The rocks of a tide pool may be

From a distance, large mounds of mussels appear as dark splotches of color against the prevailing yellowish background of the mid-coastal zone.

covered by thousands of them, packed one against the other and one atop the other, crammed together in astonishing density. Innumerable though they seem, they represent only a fraction of the millions upon millions of mussels spawned earlier in the year; the others fell victim to hungry mouths while still in the larval form, or failed to find adequate places to fasten themselves. The density of these colonies takes a further great toll on the mussels, though, for those on the bottom of the heap soon are starved or smothered. If one visits a pool that has mussels in June or July and returns to it in October, the extent of this toll becomes apparent: in a spot where 100 quarter-inch mussels could be seen in early spring, only two or three larger ones survive by autumn.

Those that live nevertheless amount to a sizable community. Even a small tide pool may house hundreds of full-grown mussels. Further perils await them, for they are a favorite food of starfish and certain snails, and if they are not eaten they may be choked by a colony of barnacles that chooses to settle right on top of them. If none of these dangers materialize, a mussel usually remains in place for several years. When the tide is high, it keeps its shell ajar, allowing the water to wash edible microorganisms into it; at low tide it closes its shell tight and stays that way until it is again submerged. Ordinarily mussels never move about, but, unlike barnacles, they can travel if they have to, even in the adult form. This is a slow process: the mussel spins a new thread of byssus, cuts the old ones with the edge of its shell, and pulls itself forward on the new one, repeating the whole procedure as often as necessary to get where it wants to go.

Mussels are found in almost every body of water in the world, both in the seas and in freshwater lakes, ponds, and streams. The ones generally seen in tide pools and on overhanging rocks at the seashore are the common or blue mussels, belonging to the genus *Mytilus*. These have dark, tapering wedge-shaped shells two to three inches long. In southern waters is found the hooked mussel, a smaller species with a curved shell. The horse mussel is a much larger form of the species *Volsella*, with a thick shell four or five inches in

The horse mussel—a bigger, thicker-shelled version of the common blue mussel—requires a moister habitat than its cousin and settles among offshore kelp forests or the lower tide pools.

length; it cannot be found in the higher and drier stretches of the shore, but lives in the lower pools and in the offshore seaweeds. Some species of mussel are used for food, especially in Europe, where the blue mussel is considered a delicacy. Hundreds of millions of pounds of mussels are consumed each year in France, Belgium, the Netherlands, and Great Britain. They are eaten also along the eastern seaboard of the United States, and sometimes on the West Coast, although eating Pacific mussels is complicated by the fact that at certain times of the year the mussels feed on organisms poisonous to man, and build up concentrations of harmful substances in their body tissues.

The sponges also belong to the class of tide-pool animals that wait for their food to come to them. They grow as crusts or mats along the sides and floors of tide pools, and their beautiful red or green or pink or yellow coloring lends a touch of gaiety to the little watery world of the pool.

Sponges are extremely simple life-forms—so primitive that for centuries they were not thought to be animals, but rather were considered plants, the nests of "sea insects," or even solidified sea foam. Aristotle, the best scientific observer of the ancient world, correctly guessed more than two thousand years ago that the ordinary household cleaning sponge is the skeleton of some sort of animal, but this was long thought to be one of that sage's errors of judgment. Late in the Eighteenth Century an Englishman, John Ellis, noticed how sponges pull water into themselves and squirt it out in jets through openings in their bodies. He demonstrated that sponges belong to the animal kingdom, but as late as 1841 at least one respected scientist still claimed they were plants.

Only the microscopic one-celled animals are simpler in design than sponges. A sponge is a loose grouping of cells, more like a colony of independent animals than a single unified creature. It lacks such organs as a stomach, gills, or lungs; it has no nervous system, no brain. The form of the body may vary, but there is always a central open space lined with cells equipped with tiny whiplike structures called *cilia*. The cilia beat constantly, drawing water into the sponge's body through the thousands of small pores that dot its outer layer. The stream of water carries food and oxygen as it passes through the sponge; bacteria and small specks of dead animals are extracted to serve as nourishment, and the water is pumped out again, taking with it the sponge's waste products.

The labor involved in this is tremendous. A sponge only four inches high must filter 25 gallons of water a day to stay alive. In order to take in enough food to gain one ounce, a sponge must draw a ton of water through its body. Though a sponge in a tide pool appears to be absolutely motionless, it is actually working hard all the time. The unseen cilia within it never rest in their task of pumping the water in.

Sponges reproduce both sexually and asexually. In sexual reproduction, some of the body cells enlarge and build up a store of food to become eggs; other become male cells or sperms. The sperms are released into the water and eventu-

ANIMAL LIFE
OF THE
TIDE POOL

39

ally pass through the pores of another sponge into the body cavity, where they meet egg cells and fertilize them. The sponge larva then develops within the parent. In certain sponges both male and female sex cells are produced by the same individual; fertilization then takes place without the necessity of having the male cells travel through the water. When the sponge larva is big enough, it escapes from the parent and swims about for a short while, finally settling in one place and attaching itself permanently.

Passive as they seem, sponges actually never stop working: to gain just one ounce these busy creatures must draw through their bodies a full ton of sea water.

In asexual reproduction, sponges reproduce by budding and branching, as plants sometimes do: they send out shoots or projections that establish themselves as new sponges, either attached to the parent or breaking loose to form independent organisms. In this way, a sponge can grow as an irregular incrustation gradually spreading over the original base, which might have been a rock, a piling, or even the back of a crab. Sponges are so simple in their structure that if they are cut to pieces, each piece will usually grow into a complete new individual.

Sponges are found in all seas and in all climates. Most of the large ones come from the tropics, where they may reach the size of a big barrel. Some sponges are composed of a tough, horny substance called *spongin*, which is strong and flexible. These are the ones that for centuries were used in homes, although today most of the sponges seen in American kitchens and bathrooms are made of plastic. Other sponges have skeletons of calcium carbonate and are as hard as stone, while some of the loveliest sponges have silica skeletons composed of interlacing needles and hairs of spun glass. These glass sponges are most common in deep water.

The sponges that live in tide pools in temperate climates are much smaller and less spectacular than those of the open sea, though they are beautiful and interesting in their own right. One of the most common is the crumb-of-bread sponge (*Halichondria panicea*), found near the low-water mark in many parts of the world. Where it is exposed to the beating of the surf, this sponge forms a thin creeping crust no thicker than a sheet of paper, spreading like a film over the rocks. But in a sheltered area such as a tide pool it becomes a dense mass several inches thick, and often sends up a host of little cone-shaped chimneys or tubes closely crowded together. The crumb-of-bread sponge derives its color from a microscopic plant that lives in its tissues. The plant thrives on sunlight, so in open pools the sponge is green or yellow, while in more secluded places shielded from the sun by rocky overhangs its color is gray-green or white. The crater-like chimneys have bright orange linings.

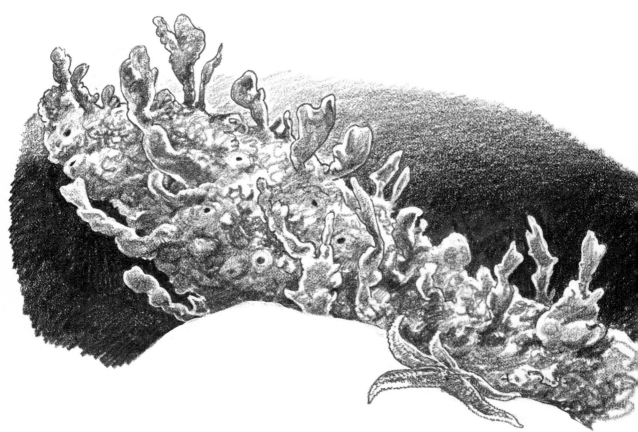

Among the most decorative creatures along the coast, the deeply-hued crimson sponge often grows in magnificent confusion with its drabber crumb-of-bread relative: a startling juxtaposition of color and form.

A deep crimson sponge, *Hymeniacidon*, often grows entangled with the crumb-of-bread sponge, creating startling blotches of vivid color. Also frequently associated with it is the eyed-finger sponge (*Chalina oculata*), a handsome rosy-pink species that grows in clusters of flat fingers bearing eye-shaped oval or circular openings scattered over their surfaces. On the sides of rocks in deep pools one may see the purse sponge, *Grantia compressa*, growing attached by a stalk. And there are scores of other tide-pool sponges forming colorful stony or rubbery encrustations as the backdrops for the rich life of the tide pool.

The tide-pool animals are by no means all as passive as the barnacles, mussels, and sponges. Over and around these permanently fixed creatures move platoons of more active organisms engaged in the ceaseless quest for food.

Many of these are univalve mollusks—which is to say that they belong to that numerous tribe, the snail family. Snails are widespread animals; they are found in the water, at the shore, and on land, living in trees and gardens. They vary greatly in size and shape, but nearly all have a single shell, usually dome-shaped or cone-shaped, that houses a soft body. A snail is equipped with a muscular flexible foot on which it glides slowly but determinedly along, and with a rasplike tongue called a *radula* used for scraping food from rocks or for drilling into other shells to get at the animal's inside. Most snails have a pair of projecting tentacles on their heads, which is believed to contain their organs of sense, touch, and sight. Attached to the foot is a horny appendage called an *operculum*, which can be pulled up tight to barricade the opening of the shell if the snail is molested or if it wishes to seal itself during a dry period.

Millions of years ago all snails were water-dwellers, but certain species have adapted to part-time or full-time life on land. The evolution of snails from marine animals to land-dwellers is still going on, and the process can readily be observed among some of the seashore's most abundant inhabitants, the periwinkles.

Periwinkles are small drab-colored snails, usually a mottled brown or gray in color, with shells that are rounded below and taper to a point. They wander unhurriedly over the seaweed-encrusted rocks, feeding on microscopic plants which they scrape loose with their radulas. As they feed, the periwinkles wear down the rocks; one scientist observed a California tide pool for sixteen years and found that the grazing periwinkles had deepened it by three-eighths of an inch during that time. That a periwinkle's radula can cause such erosion is no surprise to anyone who has viewed that organ

43

under a microscope: it is studded with hundreds of rows of minute but sturdy teeth, made of the same substance as lobster shells. One species of periwinkle has about 3500 of these teeth. The radula itself is a long ribbon, many times the length of the periwinkle's body, which is kept tightly coiled. As the teeth in front are worn down, the periwinkle rolls the radula forward to bring the next group into action.

About a dozen kinds of periwinkles are found on the coasts of North America, but three in particular that can be seen along the New England shore illustrate the evolutionary story of these animals. Near the waterline one finds the smooth periwinkle (*Littorina obtusata*). Its life is closely bound to the sea, for it can stand only brief exposure to the

The smooth periwinkle depends on nearly constant access to the sea for survival, a living reminder of the first stage in the snail family's evolutionary past.

air, and retreats under the dripping fronds of the big sea-weeds when the tide goes out. It lays its eggs in a sticky mass on the seaweed fronds; the young hatch there, complete with shells, and are immediately ready to take up life in the proper environment, on the border between land and sea.

Farther up the shore one finds a larger and more pointed snail, the common periwinkle (*Littorina littorea*). This is a hardier animal than the smooth periwinkle, and is able to tolerate fairly lengthy periods away from the water; it some-times travels past the midpoint of the beach and spends days in zones that are submerged only at high tide. Though the common periwinkle may pass more of its time in the air than under water, it, too, is biologically tied to the sea, for the young of this species are born offshore and make their way to land only when they are mature. Therefore the parent snails must descend from the high-tide rocks and go into the sea at egg-laying time.

The highest sector of the shore, from the mid-tide level to the zone that is dry except at high spring tide, belongs to the rough periwinkle (*Littorina saxatilis.*) Here we see a snail that has virtually become independent from the ocean. Its gill, unlike those of the periwinkles of the water-line, is designed to function virtually as a lung, drawing oxygen di-rectly from the air. The rough periwinkle neither casts its eggs into the sea nor fastens them to seaweeds so that they will remain submerged; instead the female periwinkle carries her eggs within her body, encased in a sort of cocoon, until they hatch. When the time arrives, great numbers of tiny, perfectly formed periwinkles emerge, each with its own miniature shell. They are born far above the waves, and take refuge in rocky crevices or empty barnacle shells until they are ready to make their own way in the upper tidal zone.

In the territory that the rough periwinkle prefers, the sea comes only once every two weeks, at the time of the high spring tide. At other times the only moisture is the spray thrown up by the waves breaking on the rocks below. The rough periwinkle is so little a creature of the sea that it can survive up to a month on dry land, and prolonged submer-

Common and rough periwinkles are both peaceful grazers but the former (at bottom), being more succulent, sometimes ends up on the gourmet's plate—a fate his less appetizing cousin manages to avoid.

sion will drown it. Evolution has carried it a long way toward becoming a full-time land-dweller. Yet the connection with the sea is not entirely broken. If it does not have at least brief exposure to water it will die; and during the course of the month it is most active during the time of high tide, becoming sluggish and feeble as the waterless interval stretches on. Scientists studying rough periwinkles in the laboratory have learned that it "remembers" the cycle of the tides even when it is no longer subjected to alternating periods of dryness and moisture; for months after it is taken from the sea, it continues to be more alert when high tide covers its native shores than when the water is low.

The passive mussel is a favorite victim of the voracious dog whelk which drills through the mollusk's shell to reach the unprotected body within.

All three types of periwinkles may be found in and around tide pools, where the normal distribution of seashore life into rigid zones does not hold true. The rough periwinkle, of course, is more likely to occupy the rocks above the pool than the pool itself, but its more water-loving cousins can be seen grazing on the plant life clinging to the sides of the pool.

Periwinkles are vegetarians, but many of the tide-pool snails feed on other animals. The brightly colored dog whelk (*Thais lapillus*) is in this class. These are large animals with thick shells several inches high. The shells vary greatly in color, apparently an effect of the whelk's diet: those that feed on mussels have purple or orange bands on a dark shell, and those that feed on barnacles are usually white.

Dog whelks live in the lower and middle zones of the tidal strip, where mussels and barnacles are most commonly found. They are moisture-loving, spending much of their time under the dripping ribbons of seaweed hanging down from the rocks. Although they sometimes eat periwinkles and other small snails, their usual victims are the stationary animals. They pierce the shells of mussels with their sharp radulas, then push their tongues through the hole to consume the animal inside. Feeding on barnacles is even easier: the whelk wraps its powerful foot over the barnacle's shell and forces the door-plates apart. At times the appetite of the dog whelks can change the balance of life over a large section of shoreline; Rachel Carson, in one of her books on sea life, tells how whelks devoured all the barnacles in one area, making room for mussels to come in and settle. When the barnacles were completely gone the whelks began to feed on the mussels. They did not know at first how to get at the new prey, but soon they were happily drilling through the mussel shells, and before very long there were no mussels left. This permitted barnacles to recolonize the area; the whelks then went back to their original and favorite food.

The egg capsules of dog whelks can be seen attached to the undersides of rock ledges or in tide-pool crevices. They are about the size and shape of a grain of wheat, and each is separately glued to the rock as part of a cluster of several dozen. It takes an hour or so for a whelk to produce one capsule; as many as ten may be deposited in a single day and several hundred in one season. Each capsule contains up to a thousand eggs, but most of these are unfertilized and will serve only as food for the developing young. After about four months the capsule breaks and 15 or 20 infant whelks come forth. The water carries them down to the lowest levels of the shore; most are swept out to sea and lost, but the strongest ones establish themselves among the seaweeds and feed on

The oyster drill may be smaller than its cousin, the dog whelk, but a more sophisticated boring mechanism helps it to satisfy its gourmet preference for that popular delicacy, the oyster.

small worms. At this stage they are about one-sixteenth of an inch high; when they reach a height of about a quarter of an inch they begin moving higher on the shore, toward the zone of barnacles and mussels where they will spend their adult lives.

The oyster drill (*Urosalpinx*) looks like a smaller version of the dog whelk. This snail, whose yellow-gray shell is about an inch in height, does tremendous damage each year to the commercial oyster beds on the Atlantic coasts of Europe and North America. A gland in the oyster drill's foot gives off a chemical that weakens an oyster's shell, making it easier to cut a hole through the shell with the radula. Since oysters are found more commonly in shallow offshore waters than in the tide-pool zone of a rocky coast, oyster drills living among the coastal rocks adapt their diets to their circumstances and feed on mussels instead. They frequently can be seen mounted on a mussel in a tide pool, patiently boring through the shell of their prey.

Dozens of other types of snails inhabit the tide-pool

world. The round-shelled ones marked with black-and-white checks that live in warm regions such as the West Indies are *neritas*; they must spend more time in water than periwinkles, but are not at all troubled by a few hours of exposure to air at low tide. Hornshells are small snails, a quarter of an inch to an inch high, with extremely narrow shells that rise in ten or fifteen spirals to a sharp point. They feed on sea plants. Smaller and somewhat similar in outline are the spindle-shaped doveshells found in the warmer sectors of both North American coasts.

There are even some snails that have no shells. These are the sea slugs—an ugly name for a beautiful creature. Sea slugs, which may be several inches in length, are soft, vulnerable-looking animals, often fantastically brilliant in color and covered by strange, elaborate projections and ornaments. They have a snail's single foot and a snail's inquisitive feelers, but must do without a snail's protective shell. When newly hatched, sea slugs have tiny spiral shells, but these disappear as the animals mature. Exposed as they are, they have other ways of warding off enemies. Most species have an unpleasant taste and are avoided by predators for that reason. One of the larger American varieties, the plumed sea slug, employs an even more remarkable way of defending itself. This slug feeds mainly on the primitive life-forms known as hydroids, which are equipped with stinging cells. When the slug eats a hydroid, the stinging cells somehow are not digested, but remain intact and migrate through the slug to its skin, where they lodge pointing outward, and will inject a fiery poison into any attacker. If such things could happen among more complex members of the animal kingdom, a snake that ate a hedgehog might sprout a coat of spines!

The plumed sea slug, which reaches a length of about four inches, bears two rows of long feathery gills all down its back, giving it a bizarre shaggy appearance. Its usual color is gray-yellow, but it takes on the hue of its food, and so may be pink, green, brown, or purple, depending on the color of the hydroids or anemones it has recently eaten. Its cousin, the bushy-backed sea slug, is even stranger to behold; this rust-

The strange beauty of the plumed sea slug is further enhanced as its normal gray-yellow hue gives way to the often brilliant color of its most recently ingested victim.

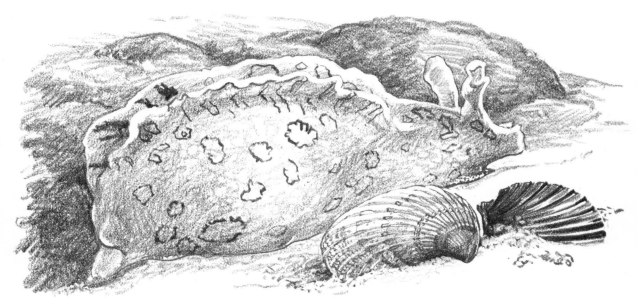

If molested, the gentle sea hare will excrete a violet-colored liquid, but for most of the time, the excellent camouflage provided by its drab coloring enables it to browse along the shoreline undisturbed.

red slug carries a dozen or more large branched plumes, its gills, sprouting from its back. A related form, the crowned sea slug, is pale yellow or pink with rusty freckles. Rising from its back are fourteen white plumes, which seem to resemble the Leaning Tower of Pisa—complete with brown dots for the windows. All of these sea slugs may be found in tide pools, and to discover one is a rare treat. Dazzling in color and strange in shape, they seem almost like visitors from another planet as they glide solemnly over the rocks.

The sea hare, a relative of the sea slugs, can sometimes be glimpsed in warm-water regions. This is perhaps the most appealing shoreline mollusk: a gentle, soft-bodied creature of the shallows, which browses peacefully through rocks and seaweeds along the shore. Sea hares can be seen at low tide and in tide pools, but one must be a keen observer to notice them, for their color provides a near-perfect camouflage. Their soft mantles, tan or greenish-yellow with dark rings, allow them to blend invisibly into the background of sea plants. Two pairs of tentacles sprout from the head, and the back pair stands upright in a rabbit-ear position that gives the sea hare its name. In the West Indies and the Florida Keys, sea hares are usually three or four inches long, but one species of Australia's Great Barrier Reef reaches lengths of more than a foot.

If molested, a sea hare will give off a "smokescreen" of violet-colored liquid, but after that one burst of irritation, which stains the water around it a delicate cranberry red, the sea hare becomes placid again. If carefully picked up and held on the palm of the hand, it will patiently wait to be returned to the water, where it will continue its browsing as though nothing had happened to interrupt its activities. If you very gently prod the sea hare's side, you can feel what remains of its shell, a firm bony mass that it carries within its body.

Clinging to the rocks in and around the tide pool is yet another distinctive kind of shoreline mollusk—the limpet. These are simple, extremely primitive snails whose shells are not coiled, but rather are broad and sloping, like the wide-brimmed hat of a Chinese coolie. The roughest waves are unable to dislodge the small animal that lives under this flattened cone of a shell; the harder the sea pounds, the more tightly the limpet's foot is pressed against the rock by the water sliding over the shell's sloping contours. Limpets exposed to the full force of the sea have higher shells than those living in tide pools and other sheltered places, apparently because they constantly need to pull down the shell with great force changes its shape.

The limpet's sticky foot, exerting a pull of up to 50 pounds a square inch, enables its owner literally to carve a niche for itself in the world. Holding tight to its rocky base, the limpet grinds the edge of its shell back and forth against the rock. This action files both the shell and the rock to an exact fit, creating a groove perfectly matched to the limpet's outline that becomes the limpet's permanent home.

Although Aristotle reported more than 23 centuries ago

**THE
WORLD
WITHIN
THE
TIDE POOL**

that limpets leave their niches and travel over the rocks, this remained a matter of doubt for many years. Eventually the question was settled by marking the shells of limpets with colored paints and keeping close watch on them. It was discovered then that limpets *do* move about. As soon as they are covered by the incoming tide they go forth, creeping slowly over the rocks for distances up to three feet from their home groove, using their radulas to scrape up particles of seaweed and smaller marine plants. Just before the tide falls they head back, and invariably are nestled into the proper niches by the time their part of the shore is exposed. The scientists found,

The limpet's sloping "coolie hat" shell and peculiar living habits (it invariably circles to the left on excursions from home) both mark this hardy creature as one of the most eccentric members of the snail family.

also, that the limpet circles to the left in the course of these expeditions, following a route that always brings it back to its starting point. Even when a limpet is pried from its rock—a difficult job—and turned around to face the opposite direction, it will usually find its way home. Only when the experimeters destroyed the fit of a limpet to its groove, either by filing the edges of the limpet's shell or by taking a chisel to the groove, did the mollusk become confused and take up a new home.

The relationship of a limpet to the groove it carves in its home rock is not merely a matter of comfort and familiarity. It is important to the limpet's survival. In order to breathe and preserve the necessary degree of moisture in its tissues, the limpet must retain some water under its shell during the hours when the tide is out. Bivalved mollusks such as mussels solve this problem by closing the two halves of their shells, while snails, although univalves, have opercula that are drawn up to the opening in the shell and make it watertight. The limpet, having a one-valved shell and no operculum, traps water by pulling itself close against its rock. This keeps a small quantity of moisture along the inner rim of the shell, where the gills are located; but if the shell does not fit perfectly against the rock, this precious moisture will escape. Therefore, the limpet goes to great pains to carve a precisely fitting groove for itself.

A number of species of limpets live in the tidal zones. All have the same general design, though some kinds have a hole at the peak of the shell, and others do not. The great keyhole limpet of the Pacific coast is the largest type, measuring up to four inches across. Atlantic limpets are usually an inch or two in diameter. Only an expert can remove a limpet from its rock without seriously damaging it.

Limpets prefer to make their homes on relatively smooth rocks, where they can achieve a good fit with little trouble. A mollusk more usually found on rough, eroded surfaces is the chiton—a living fossil, scarcely changed by evolution over millions of years. Like limpets, they carry a flattened shell on their backs and hold tightly to rocks with their single mus-

Oval in shape and armored by eight overlapping plates that give a symmetrical design to its shell, the chiton looks like a primitive artifact preserved from the ancient past.

cular foot. Chitons are oval in shape, with shells made up of eight plates that overlap from front to rear like the shingles on a roof and are held in place by tough leathery bands. Thus they present a formidable armored surface to the world. They like dark places and can be seen on the undersides of tide-pool rocks; often they burrow into eroded depressions on the rocks for further shelter. They are grazers, living on the microscopic plant life that coats their rocks. Sometimes chitons pile up, one atop the other, and each scrapes plant life from the back of the one beneath it. These unusual mollusks have a strangely primitive, ancient look, and it is not surprising to learn that fossil chitons dating back to the era of the dinosaurs are not very different in appearance from those of today. About a hundred species are found along the Pacific coast, not as many on the shores of the Atlantic. Some Pacific chitons are two or three inches in length; those of the eastern waters range from a third of an inch to an inch. Prying a chiton from its rock is a difficult job, but on some West Indian islands the natives get them loose with sharp knives, fry them, and eat them with great pleasure.

The largest mollusk likely to be found in a tide pool is an octopus. The octopus and its relative of the open sea, the squid, belong to the animal group known as *cephalopods.* That means "head-footed," and refers to the way their many tentacles sprout from the upper part of their bodies. Cephalopods are classed with the mollusks by zoologists. This seems strange at first thought, for such typical mollusks as snails and clams seem little more than blobs of living flesh, sluggish and dim-witted, while octopuses and squids are active, complex,

The formidable, vaguely sinister appearance of the octopus is misleading; it is actually just a sophisticated mollusk with the advantage of 8 "feet" or tentacles, but still cousin to the sedentary snail and clam.

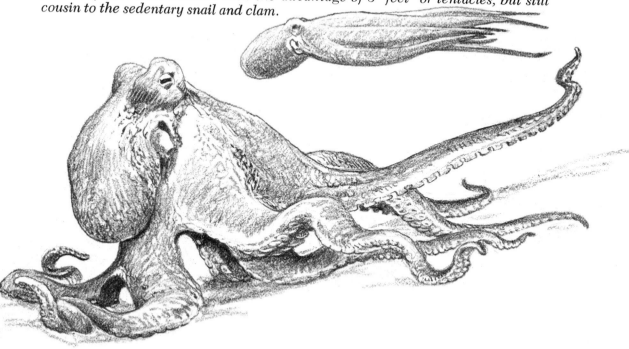

and fairly intelligent creatures. How can a clam and an octopus be considered close relatives?

Unlikely as it seems, the octopus really is nothing but a highly developed mollusk. It has many feet instead of one, but its body is soft and boneless, and it eats by scraping its food with the rasping tonguelike organ known as the radula, just as snails do. Though most of the lower mollusks are housed in shells, cephalopods have only the bare remnant of a shell, carried within the body as an internal plate.

The octopus, whose name means "eight-footed," is common in larger tide pools, but is hard to spot, for octopuses tuck themselves away in holes or crevices during the day. Only rarely are they seen, glimpsed sometimes as a tangle of brownish tentacles stirring in some dark nook. At night the octopus prowls: its eight twining, coiling tentacles are equipped with strong suckers that grab crabs or small fish and convey them toward the horny, parrotlike beak. A flabby, bag-shaped body comprises the remainder of the octopus. It has two useful defensive tactics: when irritated, it squirts a cloud of brown "ink," creating a smokescreen in the water that often allows it to escape; also it has some ability to change its color to match its background. Pigmented cells just below the skin can be rapidly expanded or contracted, causing brown or violet patches to appear on the octopus' normally pink or white body.

Every tide pool has its full quota of those agile and interesting crustaceans, the crabs. Many species are found, differing greatly from one another in size, color, and habits, but all crabs have certain basic traits in common. They carry their skeletons on the outside of their bodies—a hard leathery armor that does not grow as their bodies get bigger. When a crab's shell becomes too small for its owner, the shell cracks open and the animal abandons it, a process known as molting. For some time after molting the crab is soft and unprotected, but eventually a new shell grows and hardens. Some crabs molt ten or fifteen times during their lifetimes.

Crabs are water animals equipped with gills, although some species have adapted to life on shore, their gills having developed into simple lungs that can breathe air. Crabs have a great many jointed legs and often have one or two large claws in front. Their beady eyes, sometimes mounted on long stalks, are quite conspicuous. The diet of crabs is highly miscellaneous: some eat sea plants, some feed on fish, mollusks, and other animals, some specialize in scavenging for dead creatures, and some will eat almost anything.

Many species of crabs inhabit tide pools when young and take up a seagoing life as they get larger. Among this group are the spider crabs of the Atlantic and Pacific shores (*Libinia emarginata* and related species). These crabs have rounded bodies and long, thin, spidery legs. Their backs are

The spider crab is clumsy and sluggish. Since its jointed legs—however long and numerous—are to no avail when quick action is called for, it must depend on camouflage to elude its enemies.

**THE
WORLD
WITHIN
THE
TIDE POOL**

rough and spiny, and readily become covered with a crust of plant and animal growth—barnacles, seaweed, and other hitchhikers. This covering of small organisms serves as excellent camouflage for the spider crab as it crawls along the bottom of a tide pool. Despite their long legs, spider crabs are slow-moving and awkward, but their cousins of the Pacific coast, the kelp crabs (*Pugettia producta*) are much more alert and active. These also are long-legged crabs, somewhat smaller and less round of body than spider crabs. As their name implies, kelp crabs are common in the dense beds of kelp, the large offshore seaweeds, as well as in tide pools. Their claws are extremely strong, enabling them to cling securely to swaying fronds of kelp even when the sea is rough,

Within his large and varied family, the kelp crab is set apart by the strength of his claws, sufficient to hold fast to seaweed in even the roughest sea.

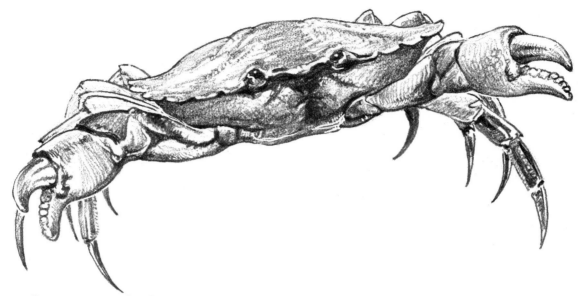

Crabs are great individualists, even among close relations: The Jonah crab, though a species of rock crab, prefers to weather both wind and waves while his namesake seeks out a quiet and sheltered home.

and anyone foolish enough to try to pick one up is likely to receive a painful nip.

Rock crabs are compact, shorter-legged animals with oval shells marked by toothy ridges around the edges. There are several species; the Jonah crab (*Cancer borealis*) is found on exposed rocks where the waves crash, the rock crab proper likes to lie hidden nearly buried in sand or gravel, and other members of this group of green, brown, or blue crabs wander through the quiet crevices of the tide pools. Rock crabs are keen-eyed and shrewd-looking, and retreat speedily from any hint of danger.

Very often at the shore you may see a snail shell walking hurriedly away from you on a host of bright red or blue legs. Snails do not have legs, so you know that what you have seen is a hermit crab. This crab (*Pagurus*), which is found in virtually every tide pool of any size on the Atlantic and Pacific coasts, lacks the customary hard outer shell of its tribe, and to shield its soft body from harm it uses a snail's discarded shell as a house, crawling backward into it with only its claws and head visible. Snail shells coil in a spiral, and the hermit crab's body is coiled the same way in back, so it fits snugly into its borrowed shell, hooking into it so tightly that it is all but impossible to remove a hermit crab without damaging it.

The first job of a newborn hermit crab is to find a shell to live in. Hermit crabs never try to evict live snails from their shells, but plenty of empty snail shells are always available. The little crab locates one of the right size, inspects it carefully with its claws to make sure it is satisfactory, and wriggles backward into it, anchoring itself in place with its curved tail and its hind legs. Tide-pool watchers are familiar with the sight of hundreds of baby hermit crabs gathered together in shells half an inch long, moving about on tiny feet. As the crab grows, problems arise. A hermit crab cannot very well molt its shell and wait for a new one to grow, as other crabs do; it must abandon its borrowed and outgrown shell and find another that is big enough for its needs.

When the unavoidable moving day arrives, the hermit crab is careful not to leave its old home until it has found a bigger shell that looks suitable. The crab then comes forth and quickly stuffs its tender body into the new shell, twisting and fidgeting to get properly settled. When the process is finished, the hermit crab can relax—until the next time. It must move many times in its life, until at last it is full grown. Big hermit crabs seek the shells of the larger snails, such as whelks or conches; baby ones generally favor periwinkle shells. Since a big hermit crab's two front nippers can inflict nasty wounds, many an unsuspecting shell-collector has had an unpleasant surprise when inspecting some attractive-looking find that happens to be inhabited by one of these hermits.

Closely related to crabs are shrimps—small swimming creatures with five pairs of jointed legs, which look something like miniature lobsters. Those that live in tide pools tend to be both transparent and extremely small, so that it takes quick eyes and a great deal of patience to catch sight of these

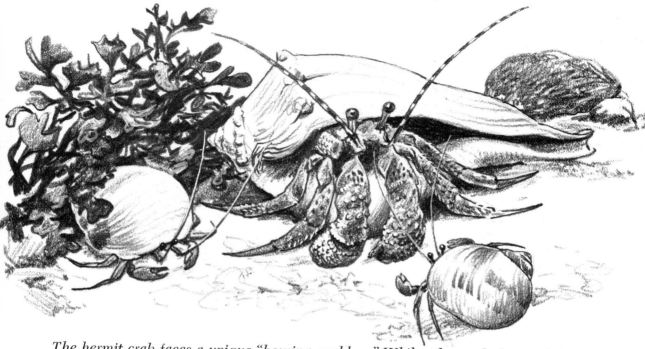

The hermit crab faces a unique "housing problem." While other crabs have a hard outer shell, the hermit crab has no natural armour of his own; instead he simply finds the right-sized snail shell and moves in.

intricate, delicate creatures. The broken-back shrimp, which gets its name from the way its back flexes as it flips its tail in its jerky backward-swimming movements, is one that may sometimes be seen. Its body is so clear that its internal organs are visible through its shell. Other members of this group range downward in size from a grain of rice to a pinhead, and are all but invisible to human eyes; they are part of the huge population of virtually microscopic crustaceans living near the surface of the sea, and as the waves wash them into the tiny pools they are devoured by most of the larger animals.

No tide-pool community is really complete without at least one representative of the animals called *echinoderms*, a name that means "spiny skins." Starfish, sea urchins, and sea cucumbers belong to this group. Most, though not all, have bristles or spines on their skins; their internal structure is more complex than that of a sponge, but less than that of a snail or a crab; and they can move about freely, if not exactly rapidly.

Starfish are found in every ocean, and at every depth from the shallows down to 15,000 feet. More than 2,000 species are known; the most common kinds are five-armed and usually red in color, but there are starfish with six, a dozen, and even fifty arms. They range in size from an inch or two in diameter, fully grown, to several feet.

The body of a starfish is nearly rigid, for it is covered with a network of stony plates; but the plates are connected by movable joints, so that the starfish is able to move its limbs. Projecting from the underside of a starfish's arms are hundreds of tube-shaped feet. To walk, the starfish pumps these tubes full of water, making them swell, and attaches the suction discs at their tips to the surface it wishes to cross. It pulls itself slowly along by letting the water out of the feet, which contracts them and hauls the starfish forward. In a tide pool a starfish travels at a rate of about fifteen feet per hour.

Starfish use their tube-feet in another way: to force open the shells of the mussels, clams, and other bivalves that are their customary food. These mollusks have powerful muscles to keep the two halves of their shells closed, but starfish are even more powerful; they wrap themselves around a bivalve and maintain a steady suction grip until the mollusk tires and lets its shell gape open. A narrow opening is all that the starfish needs. Strange as it seems, it is able to send its stomach out through its mouth and into the mollusk. It digests its prey, leaving empty shells behind, and pulls its stomach back in where it belongs.

Since starfish can devastate a bed of commercially valuable oysters, oyster fishermen regard them as enemies and kill all that they find. Once these fishermen would chop starfish into pieces and toss the fragments into the sea—but then they discovered that each piece was capable of growing into a whole new starfish! A single arm and a bit of the central body are enough to allow a starfish that has been cut up to rebuild

Colorful starfish flourish at any depth in all the oceans of the world, not only in the shallows and tide pools where their inevitable presence has made them one of the most familiar of sea creatures.

itself. Starfish also reproduce in a more conventional way, developing from eggs. Small seagoing larvae emerge, glassy-looking and equipped with slender flexible horns. They look nothing at all like starfish, but when their swimming stage is over they come ashore and undergo a transformation to the starfish shape. In the fall great numbers of young starfish can be seen, a quarter of an inch or so in diameter, hiding in the thick seaweed growths along the rocky shore.

The northern starfish, *Asterias vulgaris*, is a common denizen of Atlantic tide pools from Canada to the Carolinas. It is also known as the purple starfish, although specimens colored pink, blue, brown, yellow, or beige are nearly as abundant as purple ones. This five-armed star grows to be six

65

THE WORLD WITHIN THE TIDE POOL

to twelve inches across. Somewhat similar in size and shape is the eastern or green starfish, *Asterias forbesi*, found from Maine to the Gulf of Mexico. Despite its name it may be orange, bronze, green, purple, or brown.

The blood sea star, *Henricia sanguinolenta*, has five long, slender arms and is blood-red in color; it reaches a width of three or four inches. Fond of cold water, this starfish can be seen in tide pools from Cape Cod northward; south of Massachusetts it lives only in the deeper and colder offshore waters. It does not produce swimming larvae; instead, the female starfish humps her arms together to form a pouch in which the eggs, and later the young stars, are housed.

The most showy of the eastern starfish are the sun stars. The purple sun star, *Solaster endeca*, found northward from Cape Cod, has seven to thirteen arms, is ten to twenty inches across, and is red-violet in color. The spiny sun star,

The blood sea star lavishes unusual attention on its young: the female of this species folds her arms to create a pouch in which her offspring can develop into tiny stars, protected from the perils of the sea.

Crossaster papposus, which can be seen as far south as New Jersey, has eight to fourteen arms, and may grow to be nearly two feet in diameter. Its usual color is a brilliant scarlet, with bands of pink, crimson, or white.

Pacific tide pools provide a particularly good starfish display. Seen almost everywhere is the ochre starfish, *Pisaster ochraceus*—a crusty five-armed species more than a foot in diameter, which may be brown, orange, purple, or yellow in color. The red starfish, *Henricia leviuscula*, is a relative of the eastern blood sea star, and looks much like it, though it

The Pacific sunflower star occurs in a variety of colors ranging across the entire spectrum. Like its namesake in the flower world, this exotic multi-armed creature is a giant among its kind.

sometimes is orange or purple rather than red. Its range is from central California to Alaska.

The sunflower star, *Pycnopodia helianthoides*, found all along the Pacific coast but nowhere else in the world, is one of the giants of the starfish tribe; its broad, fleshy body, which may have as many as twenty arms, attains diameters of two to four feet. It comes in yellow and orange, red and purple, and a gray form, and inhabits the upper tide pools. Lower on the beach one may sometimes discover the western sun star, *Solaster dawsoni*, fifteen or twenty inches across, blue-gray in color with yellow borders down the edges of its ten to thirteen slender arms. This is a deep-water starfish, but occasionally is swept into shoreside pools by the waves.

An unusual Pacific starfish is the sea bat, *Patiria miniata*, which has webs between its arms, giving it a solid, compact appearance. It is generally about seven inches across and its customary colors are bright red above and yellow below, though purple or greenish ones may be seen.

Sea urchins are echinoderms without arms, whose spherical bodies are protected by limy plates joined into a rigid shell-like skeleton called a *test*. Rows of spines—blunt or wickedly sharp, long or short, stiff or flexible, depending on the species—give the sea urchin the prickly look of a living pincushion. The spines are movable and will swing about to point at a possible enemy. Like the starfish the sea urchin has hundreds of tube-feet which it fills with water and empties as it moves slowly about. Underneath the urchin is the mouth opening, with several teeth visible. It feeds on small sea animals and plants, chewing them with a complicated mill-like structure.

The rock-boring sea urchin, *Echinometra lucunter*, is found on the Atlantic coast south of Cape Hatteras. This urchin, with short black spines and a deep red body, lives in hollows and crannies in the rocks at the edge of the low-tide line. It tucks itself away in form-fitting openings hardly bigger than itself, which, so it is thought, the urchin excavates by using its spines as grinding tools; there it waits for the water to sweep food toward it. On the Pacific coast lives a similar

While all sea urchins have teeth—itself a rarity for ocean dwellers—the rock-boring urchin (left) has another grinding tool as well, his spines; easier to spot is the blunt-spined slate-pencil urchin (center) an indolent creature who will even submit to handling; in contrast, the dangerous spikes of the long-spined urchin must never be touched.

rock-boring form, the purple sea urchin, *Strongylocentrotus purpuratus.*

The slate-pencil sea urchin, *Eucidaris tribuloides,* which lives in low-level tide pools from the Florida Keys northward to the Carolinas, gets its name from its thick, stubby spines. It is a sluggish, sleepy animal that shows no objections if it is picked up in the hand to be examined; it may extend its tube-feet and wave them feebly about, but otherwise it will not react. But one urchin that is certainly not to be handled at all is the long-spined black urchin, *Diadema antillarum,* which is all too abundant on the Florida shore and in the Caribbean. Full-grown ones have bodies about four inches in diameter and spines a foot long. The slightest touch is enough to break the tip of a spine, giving one a painful splinter under the skin that easily becomes infected. Sea urchins never attack, any more than poison ivy attacks—but these urchins, nevertheless, are formidable enemies to shoreline explorers.

In more northerly waters, on the coasts of New England and the state of Washington, one finds the green sea urchin, *Strongylocentrotus droebachiensis.* These dwell by the hundreds on rock faces in the shallows, along the zone that is exposed to the air only by the lowest ebb of the tide. Their spines are extremely short and tightly packed. These urchins, which feed on periwinkles, barnacles, and sometimes mussels, are found also in the higher tide pools, wedged into crevices and hidden under boulders.

An ugly, lumpy relative of the sea urchin and the starfish is the sea cucumber, which occupies odd nooks and corners of a great many tide pools. These animals, though classed with the echinoderms, do not have spiny skins; some have thick, leathery hides, others are smooth and somewhat slimy. Sea cucumbers are sausage-shaped creatures ranging in length from a few inches to several feet. They creep about on tube-feet, pulling sand into their mouths, extracting anything edible from it, and excreting it. Since it spends all its time at this process, tons of sand pass through a sea cucumber every year.

On rocky Atlantic shores one may see the northern sea cucumber, *Cucumaria frondosa.* When covered with water

The sea cucumber, like the starfish, is adept at mobilizing his inner organs for outside use but far less skillful in retrieving them: after hurling his vitals in the face of the enemy and making his escape, this creature simply grows a new set!

this animal is five or six inches long, with a crown of waving tentacles; but should it be exposed to the air by a low tide, it curls into an inch-long football-shaped oval. A Californian sea cucumber with the same habit reaches lengths of up to eighteen inches. It is best not to disturb a sea cucumber if you find one in a tide pool, for many species cope with enemies in a startling way: with a quick contraction of its muscles the sea cucumber hurls its internal organs out of its body. It counts on this to produce a moment of confusion during which it can crawl to safety. Within a week or so, it grows a new set of organs and is apparently unharmed by its experience.

Few insects are water-dwellers, and so the most numerous of all the tribes of the animal kingdom is poorly represented in the tide-pool world. But a small salt-water insect, *Anurida maritima*, is frequently found there. The scientific name of this creature describes it well: "the wingless one who goes to sea." No bigger than a gnat, visible to us only as a minute blue-gray speck, *Anurida* is a scavenger who moves along the shore to feed on bits of crabmeat left behind by feasting gulls, on dead mussels and barnacles, on fish washed up by the tides. Though not a swimmer, *Anurida* crosses tide pools with ease to get at morsels beyond them. Its body is covered with a multitude of hairy bristles which trap a bubble of air. Wrapped in this air-blanket, *Anurida* walks lightly across the surface film of the water; a light breeze sends scores of the insects skidding and skipping over the water, bringing them together in clumps of a dozen or a hundred. When the tide rises, there is no need for *Anurida* to retreat to the safety of the dry upper shore; protected by its film of air, it stays dry under water and continues to breathe. Hiding submerged in cracks and crevices, it waits for the tide to ebb and emerges to resume its search for food.

A curious tide-pool organism, often overlooked, is the sea spider. Though these animals resemble land spiders, they are not actually closely related; zoologists are uncertain of the exact place of the sea spiders in the animal kingdom, although their jointed legs indicate a kinship to the crustaceans, insects, and true spiders. Sea spiders are mysterious little creatures, rarely more than half an inch in length including their spindly legs, and often much smaller. Four pairs of long, thin legs radiate from a small body, with a short, fifth pair in front. Creeping over the bottoms of tide pools, sea spiders suck juices from the smaller plants and animals. The males of this group have the job of taking care of the eggs, carrying them glued in sticky masses to their "egg legs" until they hatch.

Among the favorite foods of the sea spider are *hydroids* —odd, plant-like animals, part of the dense, many-colored carpet of seaweeds, sponges, and other simple organisms that encrust the tide-pool floor. A magnifying glass is useful in studying hydroids. Look down through the clear, crystalline water of a tide pool to the mossy rocks sparkling in the sunlight rebounding from the pool's bottom. On those rocks you may see little feathery plumed growths, an inch or two in height. They look like plants, but a good lens will reveal them to be something else. Hydroids are, in fact, colonies made up of a great many delicate animals such as jellyfish, sprouting on a flexible stem.

An individual member of a hydroid colony is called a *polyp*, from a Greek word meaning "many-footed." This is a reference to the numerous small tentacles fringing the polyp's mouth. Hydroids belong to the group of animals known as the *Coelenterates*, which also includes such forms as jellyfish and corals. Coelenterates are extremely simple animals that consist, essentially, of a hollow tube closed at one end. The open end of a polyp is its mouth, rimmed with the tentacles that help it to capture food. The entire hollow center of the polyp is its digestive cavity. Food enters through the mouth, is digested inside, and the waste products are spurted out the same opening through which the food entered. The polyp is made up of just two layers of cells, one layer forming the inside and one the outside of the tube.

Some coelenterates, like the jellyfish, live a free-swimming existence. The corals build permanent houses for themselves, drawing calcium carbonate from the water they live in and shaping it to form a solid structure about them; these are the coral reefs of tropical seas. Hydroid polyps collect in colonies as corals do, but build no reefs. They construct a tree-like growth permanently fastened to some object, with each polyp living in a transparent goblet-shaped cup at the tip of a branch. The colony begins when a free-swimming jellyfish-like hydroid larva attaches itself to something and sprouts a bud. The bud becomes a second hydroid, connected to the first; hundreds of other buds follow until a populous colony exists. Occasionally a bud breaks off and swims away; these are the reproductive hydroids, known as *medusae*, which release eggs or sperms into the water. When an egg is fertilized, it develops into a free-swimming larva called a *planula*, which eventually settles down and begins a new colony.

Many hydroids of great beauty live attached to the rocks, seaweeds, and even the animals of the tide pools. *Hydractinia echinata*, the pink-carpet hydroid, forms a fuzzy coating on

73

the shells in which hermit crabs live. When the crab eats, some particles of food escape its grasp and are carried within reach of the well-developed tentacles of this hydroid's polyps. Such an association is known as *commensalism*—literally, "eating from the same table." Several other species of hydroids live on the shells of hermit crabs.

The kelp hydroid, *Obelia geniculata*, is common in tide pools on both the Atlantic and Pacific coasts. It is a fragile plantlike form, rarely more than an inch in height. *Obelia commissuralis*, a related hydroid, is a busy one six to eight inches high with a zigzag stem; a lens shows that its polyps are protected by bell-shaped cups. It is found on the east coast of North America. Another eastern form is *Sertularia pumila*, whose main stem forms a tangled mass crossing and recross-

This organism—to all appearances a plant—is actually a group of extremely primitive animals, the hydroid obelia; the task of pioneering new communities falls to the larger fertile polyps which are able to start a new colony on their own.

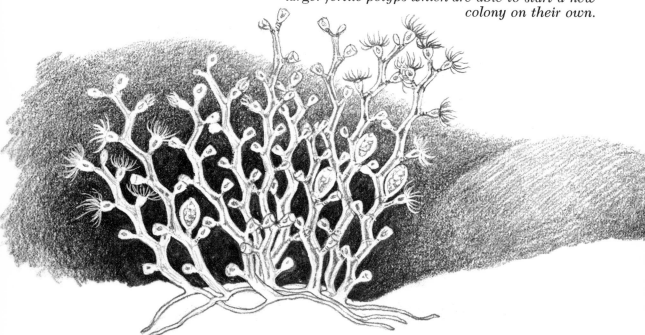

Growing as a crusty, cream-colored coating on rock surfaces, this bryozoan (Membranipora) sets off the swaying filigree and velvet carpet formed by the other moss animals on the tide pool floor.

ing itself. Though the only apparent motion of a hydroid is its swaying with the flow of the water, its polyps are forever at work seizing and devouring hordes of microorganisms beyond the scope of the human eye.

A second group of small, delicate "seaweeds" on the tide-pool floor also belongs to the animal kingdom. These are the *Bryozoa*, a name that means "moss animals." Commonly called sea mats or sea laces, they are similar to hydroids but are not related to them. Although they live in colonies, the individual bryozoans are virtually independent of one another, whereas the lives of all the polyps in a hydroid colony are closely interconnected.

One species, *Bugula turrita*, the fern bryozoan, forms fluffy upright plantlike growths easily mistaken for seaweeds. Another, *Aetea anguina*, sends up erect club-shaped spikes from creeping horizontal stems visible to us as networks of white threads. Others, such as the sea lace bryozoan, *Menbranipora pilosa*, grow as flat stony crusts on rocks and seaweed fronds. These brittle little growths, white or cream-colored, enhance the beauty and complexity of the tide-pool background.

The gaudy sea anemones bring a different touch of floral beauty to the tide pool. Though they look like flowers, sea anemones are animals, classed with the coelenterates. They are much larger than hydroid or coral polyps, sometimes reaching diameters of a foot or more, but their structure is basically the same: a hollow tube with a mouth and tentacles at one end.

The tentacles give the sea anemones their name. They are brightly colored, thick, and fleshy, almost like the petals of a flower. Often they are the only visible part of the anemone, for the sturdy tubular body is usually hidden in sand or in a cranny of the rocks. The lovely petals wave enticingly, and any small animal that comes near will find their attractiveness a deadly snare, for stinging cells wait to paralyze and capture anything edible.

Surprisingly, though, certain crustaceans and fish live right within reach of the tentacles of some big anemones of the tropics, and are unharmed by the stinging cells. The fish are brightly colored, two or three inches long; they snuggle into the tentacles, hiding in their folds, and even venture into the anemone's stomach at times. Shrimps and crabs associated with giant anemones are usually transparent and nearly invisible, but occasionally they, too, are bright in color. Sheltered by the anemone's stinging tentacles, these little creatures are safe from attack. Scientists think they serve their hosts as scavengers, cleaning away the waste fragments of the creatures the anemone eats. Why they are immune to the stings remains a mystery.

Another odd partnership involves crabs and anemones. One kind of large hermit crab allows small stinging anemones to attach themselves to the outside of its shell. Seven or eight anemones may ride the same shell, serving as a battery

These lovely anemones are masters at the art of seduction: their undulating petal-like tentacles lure appetizing passersby within reach of their stinging cells which then paralyze the victim.

of living machine-guns for the crab. Their stinging cells ward off the crab's foes, while the anemones benefit by eating discarded scraps of the crab's meals. When the time comes for the hermit crab to move to a bigger shell, it takes its anemones with it, carefully detaching them with its claws and transferring them to the new shell. This anemone, *Adamsia*, is most common on the South Atlantic coast.

Anemones are able to move from place to place. Usually they remain rooted to the same spot for weeks or months, though they may creep slowly away in search of more favorable quarters. Anemones are extremely long-lived; some have survived 75 years or more in aquariums. They reproduce by laying eggs or simply by splitting in half, each half becoming a complete new anemone. Sometimes the eggs are kept inside the female until they hatch. One anemone, which lived for 66 years in a British aquarium, gave birth in this way to over 700 living young, and on one startling occasion produced 230 offspring in a single night.

Anemones are handsome features of many tide pools. Customarily they are found on the pool floor, but some prefer a vertical life, attaching themselves to the sides of protected overhanging ledges. When the tide is low an anemone is a dismal sight; those on flat surfaces pull themselves tightly together, becoming drab rubbery lumps, and those on vertical rock faces hang down, limp and soggy. But when the water returns they "bloom" magnificently, expanding their pliable bodies and unfolding their gorgeous crowns of tentacles.

A vivid anemone of Pacific tide pools is *Anthopleura xanthogrammica*, bright green in color, taking its emerald hue from microscopic plants that live in its tissues. Hundreds of them may be seen in a single pool. The red anemone, *Corynactis californica*, found from San Francisco to San Diego, is another beautiful species. On the East Coast the brown anemone, *Metridium dianthus*, can be found from Maine to New Jersey. Dark chocolate-brown in color and up to four inches high, it may have as many as a thousand white tentacles. A smaller and more delicate species is *Sagartia leucolena*, an inch or two in height and a translucent pink-white in color; its tentacles are slender and supple. Because it is very sensitive to light, it can be discovered only in dark corners of the tide pools. There are scores of others, ranging in size from half an inch or so to much greater diameters, and displaying all the colors of the rainbow.

We have not begun to exhaust the animal life of the tide pool in this chapter. A host of other forms can be found in the pools—tube worms and scale worms, sea squirts, jellyfish, arrowworms, and many more, as well as the numerous small fishes who flit through the tide-pool world. It would be impossible to discuss all of them here. But in these pages we have at least hinted at the immense multitude of living creatures who make their homes in that narrow zone between the sea and the land.

ANIMAL LIFE
OF THE
TIDE POOL

4

Plant Life
of the
Tide Pool

THE kingdom of plants, like that of animals, has been arranged by scientists into a series of classifications that depend on complexity of form. We have already examined the outline of the animal kingdom: one-celled protozoa are the simplest animals, and then come the sponges, the corals and other coelenterates, the starfish and related echinoderms, and so forth up through the worms, bryozoans, mollusks, crustaceans, and insects to the life-forms of the most elaborate structure—the fishes, amphibians, reptiles, birds, and mammals.

In the plant kingdom the primitive one-celled organisms known as bacteria occupy the lowest place. Above them are the algae—the group of seaweeds and drifting water plants— and then the fungi, including mushrooms and molds. Next come mosses, ferns, and such lesser-known forms as horsetails and club mosses; lastly, there are the seed-bearing plants and trees.

While eelgrass (often confused with common seaweed) is not visually impressive it enjoys the distinction of being one of the rare flowering plants that can support an underwater existence.

Although the higher animals are absent from the miniature world of the tide pool, they are no strangers to the ocean at large. Every group of the animal kingdom is represented in the marine world, even the birds and mammals; penguins are birds that spend most of their lives in the water, and whales and dolphins are seagoing mammals. But the sea is far poorer in types of plant life than the land. Within the tide pools or outside them, almost the only plants to be found belong to one of the simplest groups, that of the algae. The sea has no trees and hardly any flowering plants. Among the few species in this category is eelgrass, *Zostera marina*, a green plant with ribbonlike leaves that grows under water just off the coast. Though it can easily be mistaken for a seaweed, eelgrass bears small flowers along the blades of some of its leaves, something no seaweed does. Evidently the ancestors of eelgrass developed on land, and the habit of flowering is all that remains to show the plant's ancient habitat. The flowers are sterile, though, and eelgrass reproduces by sending out shoots from its roots. Virtually all the other plants one finds in the sea are algae.

Algae are considered simple plants because the cells making up their bodies are not specialized into roots, stems, and leaves, as in higher plant forms. Growing submerged in water which is rich in dissolved minerals, each cell of an alga absorbs what it needs for itself. Nor do algae produce flowers and seeds. They reproduce by forming small one-celled bodies known as spores, or by splitting into fragments, each fragment of the parent growing into a new plant. They also sometimes reproduce by releasing eggs and sperm cells.

It is important to realize that *simple* does not mean *small*. Algae come in all sizes, from the microscopic to giant kelps a hundred feet long or more. A little dandelion is more complicated than an immense kelp, however, because of its system of producing flowers, getting them fertilized, and growing seeds. Algae existed on the earth for many millions of years before evolution produced such complex forms as the flowering plants.

There are some 18,000 species of algae. Some drift freely on the surface of the water, but most are fixed, growing attached to underwater rocks, other plants, even the bodies of animals. They hold themselves in place with root-like structures known as *holdfasts*. True roots are tubes through which a plant obtains nourishment; algae have no such structures, and their holdfasts are merely tendril-like growths serving as anchors.

Botanists divide the algae into five main groups, distinguished by their structure and habitat and particularly by their color. Though all algae contain the green pigment, chlorophyll, that is essential in a plant's energy-manufacturing process, they contain other pigments as well which give the different groups their characteristic colors. Examples of

Sea lettuce is the largest and most plentiful of the green algaes: the plant's emerald-green, elaborately convoluted fronds are a familiar adornment along the entire length and breadth of the tidal strip.

all five groups can be found in the tide-pool world, though some are more conspicuous than others.

The blue-green algae (*Cyanophyceae*) are the simplest kind. Many of them are one-celled floating organisms. Blue-green algae form a fuzzy or slimy scum covering seashore rocks and pilings and the surface of the sea itself. They can thrive in polluted water and in waters too hot for other plants; blue-green algae grow in the hot springs of Yellowstone National Park at temperatures close to the boiling point of water. Blue-green algae are not always blue-green;

the Red Sea gets its name from one, *Trichodesimum erythraeum*, which periodically increases its numbers greatly and covers the surface of that sea with a coloring of yellow, orange, or red. Other blue-green algae contain such quantities of the blue pigment, phycocyanin, that they appear black or brown. Algae of this sort are found as a thin crust covering the rocks of the uppermost zone of the tidal strip, where the rough periwinkles prowl, and it is these plants that give that zone its typical brownish-black color.

The yellowish-green algae (*Chrysophyta*) are another tribe of small free-floating plants. Most of them are microscopic and, while present in tide pools, are not readily apparent to human observers. Included in this group are the handsome organisms known as diatoms, which have beautiful glassy shells, and the odd dinoflagellates, plants that behave something like animals and propel themselves through the water with a pair of whip-like organs.

The algae found highest on the shore and most abundantly in the tide pools are the green algae (*Chlorophyceae*). These seaweeds, generally a delicate pale green in color, grow as lacy strands, branching fronds, or silky fringed filaments. The sea lettuces (*Ulva lactuca* and *Ulva lastissima*) are the most familiar members of this group. Their thin, wrinkled, emerald-green fronds are found all up and down the shore from the low-tide mark to the high pools. Largest of the green algae, the sea lettuces reach lengths of three to four feet, though they are much smaller in some pools, with leaves six to eight inches long. The resemblance to true lettuce is extraordinary.

Codium or sponge seaweed is another common type on both North American coasts. Its many branching stalks have a soft, spongy texture. Close kin to it is sea moss, *Bryopsis*, which has about twenty species on the two coasts; it has a delicate, feathery look. *Cladophora*, called mermaid's tresses, lives on the north Atlantic coast; it forms small tufted plants that look like miniature bushes in tide pools. In the warmer waters of the southern Atlantic and Gulf of Mexico coasts one finds the odd *Penicillus*, the merman's shaving brush.

THE WORLD WITHIN THE TIDE POOL

"Penicillus" is Latin for a small brush, and that is exactly what this green alga seems to be: two to five inches long, it stands upright and has a thick whitish-green stalk topped by stiff brush-like filaments.

The brown algae (*Phaeophyceae*) include some of the largest and most frequently encountered of the seaweeds. These somber-looking plants prefer cold water and generally are found offshore, at depths ranging down to forty or fifty feet, but some members of the group are among the most conspicuous species of vegetation in the tidal strip.

Sometimes the pools of the upper third of the shore are lined with a velvety brown coating, which can be peeled from the rocks in thin papery sheets. This is a brown seaweed known as *Ralfsia verrucosa*, which provides shelter for some

The spiral wrack is a type of algae found in great abundance along the Atlantic coast. Well adapted to a land environment, this hardy rockweed anchors itself to ledges seldom reached by the incoming tides.

of the smallest creatures of the tide-pool world. One scientist who paid special heed to this alga was Rachel Carson, who wrote in *The Edge of the Sea*, "Looking at these pools with their velvet lining, one would say there is little life here—only a sprinkling of periwinkles browsing, their shells rocking gently as they scrape at the surface of the brown crust, or perhaps a few barnacles with their cones protruding through the sheet of plant tissue, opening their doors to sweep the water for food. But whenever I have brought a sample of the brown seaweed to my microscope, I have found it teeming with life. Always there have been many cylindrical tubes, needle-fine, built of a muddy substance. The architect of each is a small worm whose body is formed of a series of eleven infinitely small rings or segments, like eleven counters in a game of checkers, piled one above another. . . . And always, among this microfauna of the Ralfsia crust, there have been little fork-tailed crustaceans with glittering eyes the color of rubies. Other crustaceans called ostracods are enclosed in flattened, peach-colored shells fashioned of two parts, like a box with its lid. . . . But most numerous of all are the minute worms hurrying across the crust—segmented bristle worms of many species and smooth-bodied, serpent-like ribbon worms or nemerteans, their appearance and rapid movements betraying their predatory errands." In just this way do the seaweeds of the shore contain whole universes of life.

Certainly no rocky shore in the temperate zone is without its representative of the widespread genus of brown algae called *Fucus*. There are a number of species of *Fucus*, known popularly as rockweed; the plant is one of the most widely distributed living things in the world. It can be recognized by its olive-green or yellowish-brown color, by its twisted leathery fronds, and most particularly by the small berry-like air-bladders that break with little popping sounds when you squeeze them between your fingers.

The rockweeds illustrate evolution's diversity. Though spawned in the sea, they have invaded the shore and have moved up and up the tidal strip, with some species able to occupy the regions where water seldom reaches. Today we find *Fucus* and related rockweeds at all levels of the shore, each species well adapted to the special conditions of its particular zone.

A European rockweed, the channeled wrack (*Pelvetia caniculata*), inhabits the uppermost edge of the tidal strip. Its narrow yellow fronds form a band three to five feet in breadth along the high-water line, and much of the time the only moisture it receives is an occasional burst of spray. During prolonged periods of exposure to air the channeled wrack's fronds wither and turn black, so that the plant appears to be dead, but when the spring tide comes it resumes its normal color and rubbery texture.

The channeled wrack's counterpart on the American side of the Atlantic is a related form, *Fucus spiralis*, the spiral wrack. This plant ventures nearly but not quite as far into the world of land life. Its short, broad orange-brown fronds, studded by rough-textured swellings, grow most heavily on ledges just above the high-water mark of the near tide. Thus it spends up to three quarters of its existence out of the water.

Lower on the shore, thick festooned clusters of rockweeds that are more water-loving hang gracefully down, forming dense, fringed curtains over the face of the rocks. Where the surf is not too violent the knotted wrack, *Ascophyllum nodosum*, flourishes. In quiet bays and inlets the slender fronds of this rockweed reach lengths of six to seven feet or more; they are distinguished by the single row of air-bladders down their centers. The knotted wrack cannot endure the heavy pounding of strong waves, however, and in this level of exposed coasts it is replaced by a shorter-fronded, tougher species, *Fucus vesiculosus*, the bladder wrack. This species has a double row of air-bladders to help it remain buoyant when the tide is in, although the bladders may fail to develop on the small, stunted plants that grow where the surf is heaviest. These rockweeds often are ripped loose by the fury of the waves, but *Fucus* fragments continue to grow as they drift, and if they lodge in a favorable place may send out new holdfasts and take up permanently fixed life again.

Below the level of the knotted wrack and the bladder

Along sheltered regions of the coast thick growths of the knotted wrack droop from the rocks, its long slender fronds forming a natural barrier at the juncture between land and sea.

wrack is the low-water line, covered by the tides except at the time of lowest ebb. Here we find the most densely thriving rockweeds of all. *Fucus furcatus*, the popping wrack, represents the family north of Cape Cod and on the northern Pacific coast. *Fucus edentatus*, the worked wrack, or *Fucus serratus*, the notched wrack, are found elsewhere. Thus we have a cascade of rockweed from the highest to the lowest points on the shore, creating a dark and tangled forest through which a multitude of crabs and whelks and other shoreline creatures pursue their daily routines.

At the sea itself, the rockweeds give way to their giant relatives, the kelps, *Laminaria*. These massive plants, the Sequoias of the sea, dominate the offshore waters of both North American coasts. Some, such as *Nereocystis* and *Macrocystis* of the Pacific, attain lengths of several hundred feet. But though the kelps are fascinating organisms—and useful as well, for they are important foods in Asia, are used in many lands as fertilizers, and yield substances employed in the making of ice cream, chocolate milk, and medicines—

89

most of them are too big to be part of the tide-pool community. However, kelps are sometimes found in very deep pools at the lowest levels of the shore. Their mighty holdfasts become dwelling-places for all kinds of marine animals: sponges and urchins, starfish and mussels, hydroids and bryozoans, even the uncommon, fragile, long-armed echinoderms known as brittle stars. All these and more find niches for themselves in the branching and tangling anchors of the great seaweeds, while above them the flat brown ribbons of the kelp spread out grandly over the surface of the pool.

The last of the five groups of algae is the red algae (*Rhodophyceae*), which are almost entirely deep-water forms, although some members of the group inhabit tide pools. The red algae are smaller in size than the brown ones, the largest species reaching lengths of about six feet. They contain a pigment called phycoerythrin which gives them their characteristic and beautiful red or violet coloring. This pigment is capable of absorbing the blue and ultraviolet solar rays that penetrate the sea to depths of 50 to 100 feet, where light of other colors is screened out by the water. Thus seaweeds containing phycoerythrin are able to carry on their life-processes at depths where other seaweeds would perish from lack of usable light. The most purely red of the red algae live at the greatest depths.

Among the most elegant of the red algae that a low tide exposes in the lowest tide pools are those belonging to the genus *Dasya*. This is a Greek word meaning "hairy," and the many species of *Dasya* found on the Atlantic and Pacific coasts do indeed seem covered with fine rose-red hair. Growing in quiet, sheltered areas of the shore, the plant forms slender stems two or three feet long that are clothed in short, silky, hair-like branches. When taken from the water this beautiful alga collapses into a slimy jelly-like mass.

Dulse, *Rhodymenia palmata*, is a red seaweed that is prized for its nutritional value in many countries. Found along the shores of the Atlantic and the Mediterranean at the low-tide line and in tide pools, dulse grows in the form of thin, tough, elongated flat fronds, indented so that they look

Prickly sea urchins cluster around the holdfasts of the giant kelps (Laminaria) which also provide shelter for a host of other small sea creatures.

vaguely like hands. These flutter in the water and, when the tide is out, pile up on one another in matted layers. Icelanders dry the fronds of dulse in the sun and eat them either raw or boiled with milk and flour. In Scotland dulse is used as a relish, as a substitute for chewing-tobacco, and as a medicine. Norwegians call it sheep's-weed because sheep and cattle wander down to the shores at low tide to search for it, preferring its flavor to that of grass.

Another edible red seaweed is purple laver or purple sea lettuce, the common name of the various algae belonging to the genus *Porphyra*. It grows in both hemispheres and in all waters from the Arctic to the tropics. Its fronds, which have the shape of lettuce leaves and range from pale lavender to purple-brown in hue, are thin and delicate-looking, though they are tougher than they seem to be; one scientist compares the fronds of a Maine variety to "nothing so much as little pieces of brown transparent plastic cut out of someone's raincoat." American Indians were fond of eating *Porphyra tenera*, found along the Pacific Coast from California to Alaska. In the British Isles, purple laver is boiled with vinegar to become a jelly that is spread on toast, and is made also into fried cakes. Hawaiians know it as a delicacy called *limu*,

91

Two red algae, dulse and Irish moss, contain a special pigment enabling them to survive at far greater depths than the common surface kelps. It also produces their impressive regal coloring.

eaten fresh and crisp, or salted and preserved. In Japan it is used as a flavoring for soups and meats.

The stubby little seaweed known as Irish moss or carrageen (*Chondrus crispus*) lines many tide pools and creates a thick, rich, lustrous matting on rocks at the low-tide line. Usually deep red or chocolate-brown, though sometimes violet or greenish-purple, Irish moss is low-growing and branches profusely. Exposed only briefly by the retreating tides, it holds moisture well, and the dense cushions of Irish moss on the low rocks house a busy community of hydroids, bryozoans, starfish, urchins, and periwinkles. This red alga has considerable value to man; on the coasts of New England and Europe, fishermen can be seen raking up boatloads of it and putting it out to dry in the sun. A gluey substance called *carrageenin* is extracted from the dried fronds and is used in candies, jellies, puddings, and other foods. Carrageenin is also an industrial chemical, employed in curing leather, in shampoos, and as an ingredient of shoe polishes and shaving creams.

Gelidium, which reaches lengths of about six inches on rocks on the north Atlantic Coast, is a maroon or purple-brown seaweed with flat, horny branches that is the chief source of agar-agar, used in bacteriological research for growing cultures of microorganisms. In Japan it is also made into jellies, soups, sauces, and deserts. *Gigartina*, a stringy, spiny red plant of the Pacific shore, is harvested commercially for its chemical value. A flattened leaf-like red seaweed, *Dilsea*, was the source of the rouge used by the women of ancient Greece and Rome.

We can see, then, that although the world of the tide pools and rocky shores can offer us only the most primitive plants on earth, we still may find a rich assortment of strange and attractive vegetation. On the margin of the sea peculiar forests thrive, where the familiar green of plant life is a rarity and the dominant hues are warm browns and brilliant reds—where leaves and roots and flowers are unknown, and the bizarre plants of the water, dancing and swaying to the rhythm of the tides, display shapes and forms and textures of an alien and oddly beautiful kind.

5

The
Tide Pools
in Peril

THE tide-pool world is a place of wonder and en-
chantment, a sparkling, self-contained universe within a
small span. We go down to it in awe and delight, and come
away refreshed and exhilarated by what we have seen. But
how much longer will our shores offer such ready pleasures?
Is a time coming when one will be able to explore tide pools
only in a few fortunate remote corners of the world?

Early in the nineteenth century Lord Byron, in his long
poem *Childe Harold's Pilgrimage*, addressed these lines to
the boundless, heaving sea:

> Roll on, thou deep and dark blue ocean, roll!
> Ten thousand fleets sweep over thee in vain;
> Man marks the earth with ruin—his control
> Stops with the shore.

*Man marks the earth with ruin. His control stops with
the shore.* Alas, what may have been true a century and a half

Pollution-killed fish: A welcome feast for birds of prey, no doubt, but we can ill afford the tremendous damage to marine life caused by the wanton dumping of industrial waste.

ago holds true no longer. Man has carried his trail of ruin past the boundaries of his own domain, the land, and has begun to cover the sea as well with destruction. The effects of the mindless, unending pollution that the spread of humanity has brought to the global environment have begun to be registered along our coasts, and the small inhabitants of the tide pools are among the victims.

Consider the intrusions, huge or trifling, that we make upon the life of the shore. We amuse ourselves with pleasure-boats that zoom up and down the coasts, leaving murky trails of waste fuel to drift toward the land. Our rivers run thick with the outpourings of chemicals from industrial plants, flooding into the sea to poison all life-forms for miles around. Picnickers choke entire beaches with mounds of beer-cans and other debris. Raw sewage pours into the ocean, smothering its living things in filthy muck. From our coastal power plants come torrents of hot water, raising the temperatures of shoreline regions beyond tolerable levels. On the coast of southern California alone, at least 50,000 industrial plants are contributing to the contamination of the sea. They include plastic factories, petroleum refineries, metallurgical plants, and a variety of other installations, among them the Norton Air Force Base, which each year dumps 1.8 million gallons of chromium and cyanide compounds, as well as other poisonous wastes. In a thousand different ways a day we launch savage assaults on our shores, disrupting the fragile balance of life, shattering that delicate network of natural relationships that constitutes the marine ecology. In the United States, 75 percent of the population lives in states bordering the coastline, and nearly 45 percent lives right on the coast. The strain that this concentration of humanity imposes on the life of the adjoining sea is intense and crushing. Our pollution spreads death and devastation on all levels from the microscopic to the gigantic. Somber tentacles of poisonous fluid steal into the lairs of the octopus and the clam, the barnacle and the starfish, sparing no form of life. A complex, beautiful world, living in nature's perfect balance, is being strangled and slaughtered by an army of pollutants.

The unchecked and unregulated growth of human society is destroying the coasts and wiping out the small, inoffensive creatures of the tide pools at a terrifying rate.

The disturbances we create in the ecological balance are often subtle ones. Once, for example, there were tremendous forests of kelp just off the California coast, housing a vast and intricate community of maritime creatures. Late in the 1940's the stands of kelp closest to the shore began to die. Within ten years huge regions were virtual deserts. The Point Loma kelp forest off San Diego, which had covered six square miles, shrank to a patch little more than half a square mile in area. The Palos Verdes forest off Los Angeles, formerly extending through three square miles, disappeared almost entirely. With the vanishing of the great kelp, the animal community that had taken shelter in it also departed. Not only was a commercially valuable seaweed wiped out, but the whole coastal environment was impoverished.

Scientists studying the sudden kelp decline pointed to human sewage as the villain. Every day the cities of southern California pour half a million gallons of sewage into the off-shore waters. This foul stream contains not only human urine and excrement, but the acids and brines and dyes and other chemical wastes of industry. Was this river of poison blighting the kelp? That seemed obvious—until studies done at California's Scripps Institution of Oceanography showed that kelp actually seemed to thrive on a diet of sewage.

What, then, was causing the trouble? Scientists in diving gear went into the kelp forests to see. Exploring the holdfasts of the kelp, a hundred feet down and more, they were startled to discover millions of purple sea urchins clustered on the bottom. An urchin, nibbling on the holdfast of a kelp with its five small, sharp teeth, can eventually cut through the tough fiber. Many urchins nibbling on the same plant could sever all its holdfasts, uprooting the kelp and setting it adrift. But in the past the urchins had been scattered, a few dozen here, a few dozen there—never enough to imperil an entire kelp forest. Now they swarmed like insatiable ants in uncountable numbers around the holdfasts.

The damage caused by oil spills is immediate and highly visible. Less publicity but no less danger is associated with the flushing procedure, a matter of routine "house cleaning" among ships which releases great quantities of toxic oil.

Laboratory research showed that the urchins were absorbing organic matter, particularly amino acids, to an unusually high degree. The source of the organic matter was the sewage discharges. Far from poisoning the coastal waters, the sewage was acting as fertilizer for the urchins, feeding them and stimulating them to reproduce in great quantities. The effect was to create an unbalanced ecology: there were too many urchins, and they were destroying all the kelp. The proof came when an oil tanker stranded on the coast of Lower California dumped its cargo into the sea. The oil killed all the urchins in the area; and, within a year, the kelp was able to reestablish itself.

If we are unable to predict the consequences of our acts —if our casual spilling of sewage wrecks the maritime ecology not by poisoning life but by stimulating it to explosive growth—how can we guard against similar calamities in the future? The kelp foresters of California solved their problem by dumping quicklime into the sea from barges. This was fatal to the urchins; once they were dead, healthy kelp plants were brought from other parts of the sea and embedded to become the nucleus of a new forest. But what will keep the urchins from creeping back into the kelp forests in another few years? More quicklime will have to be dumped then. What if the quicklime proves to have some destructive effect, not yet observed, on the coastal environment? We tamper and then tamper again with what was once a self-sustaining world. To counteract our sewage outflow we dump quicklime; will the quicklime require some remedy also? And when will our interference with the environment put matters beyond nature's powers of renewal?

New and unpleasant ecological surprises confront us all the time. In Holland, in 1965, great masses of dead fish were washed ashore on the beaches at Noordwijk on the North Sea. Scientists from the Netherlands Institute for Fisheries Investigation detected some attractive blue crystals on the scales of the fish, and identified the blue substance as copper sulphate. Analysis showed that the copper content of the coastal sea was 500 times greater than normal. Some factory had dumped a large quantity of this poisonous copper compound into the ocean; perhaps the dumping had taken place far inland, and the deadly blue crystals had been swept to the sea by a river. The offshore currents, instead of distributing the copper sulphate through the vast body of the ocean and thus diluting it to a harmless concentration, held it pinned against one stretch of the coast, with tremendous local impact on maritime life. Then a shift in the currents began to move the stuff away from Noordwijk—to another part of the coast where valuable beds of mussels were cultivated. But still another change in the flow of the currents sent the contaminated water out to sea before further harm was done.

DDT, a chlorinated hydrocarbon widely sprayed on land to control undesirable insects, is now helping to make the sea uninhabitable. Rain washes DDT into rivers, and the rivers carry it to the ocean; a report issued by the National Academy of Sciences in June, 1971, asserts that close to a quarter of all the DDT manufactured to date is now in the sea, and, the report declares, "Marine fish are almost universally contaminated with chlorinated hydrocarbon residues."

Those forms of marine life most closely related to insects —lobsters, crabs, and shrimps—are killed outright by DDT. It renders the eggs of certain fish sterile: off the coast of southern Texas, the density of speckled sea trout declined from 30 an acre in 1964 to 0.2 an acre in 1969, while the residue of DDT in trout eggs was rising from insignificant levels to a figure of eight parts per million. Such organisms as oysters and mussels are able to take in astonishing quantities of DDT without suffering ill effects; but, by accumulating it in their tissues, they pass it along in concentrated form to those animals, including man, that feed on them. Thus DDT contamination travels up the food chain and the insecticide builds up in potentially dangerous quantities in the bodies of predatory creatures.

No area of the world seems exempt from the DDT plague. Scientists in the Antarctic found high concentrations of DDT in the bodies of penguins and seals. No crop-spraying programs had been active in the vicinity of the South Pole; rather, ocean currents and rain-bearing clouds had carried particles of DDT to the icebound continent, where it had been consumed by the fish and shellfish on which the penguins and seals fed.

DDT is not the only insecticide that makes its way to the sea. Aside from the insect-killers, we have been polluting the sea with deadly mercury, dumped in large amounts by certain industries, and with equally poisonous lead, which gets into the air as part of automobile exhaust and falls with the rain into our oceans. The annual lead fallout in the North Pacific and North Atlantic is presently about half a million *tons* a year. This has enormously increased the degree of lead pollution in the sea, particularly in coastal areas. Sea bass caught off the California coast near smog-choked Los Angeles have been found to have an average content of 22 parts of lead for each million parts of liver tissue—double to triple the normal amount. Even 200 miles off shore, the Pacific near Los Angeles contains 18 times as much lead as does the middle of the Mediterranean and 50 times as much as the Atlantic near Bermuda. This automobile-generated outpouring of lead along the coasts is thought to be in part responsible for a recently observed outbreak of cancerous growths, skin ulcers, and other malformations among the shore-dwelling fishes of the United States.

Then, too, since the advent of the atomic age we have been disposing of unwanted radioactive substances by sealing them in oil drums, weighting the drums with cement, and sinking them at sea. The drums, apparently, often break in the depths. Yet we go on dumping them—along with old trolley cars, demolished slum buildings, unwanted chemicals, and cargoes of "surplus" military poison gases. How long can the oceans, gigantic as they are, endure this steady diet of chemicals and radioactivity and debris before becoming unfit for life?

If we do not destroy the maritime ecology by poisoning it, we are likely to choke it with oil. The energy needs of mankind grow frenziedly from year to year, and oil is one of our prime sources of energy. Since the areas that consume the most oil are not necessarily the areas where the most oil is found, giant tankers ply the seas, some of them carrying up to 300,000 tons of oil. And sometimes those tankers have accidents.

On March 18, 1967, the tanker *Torrey Canyon* ran aground on a reef off the southwest coast of England. The ship was only of medium size as the new tankers go; it carried a cargo of 117,000 tons of oil—more than 36 million gallons—from Arabia. As the huge hull split open, the oil began to spill into the sea. Dark, glistening slicks spread from the scene of the wreck and within three days covered a hundred square miles of water. One great slick, 18 miles long, drifted toward the shores of Cornwall, and soon engulfed a stretch of beach more than 100 miles in length in a slimy, murderous black coating. Thousands of shore birds, trapped in the sticky mass of oil, suffocated despite the efforts of Britishers who attempted to free them and clean their feathers. The complex, delicate inhabitants of the tidal zone—anemones, urchins, barnacles, mussels, clams, crabs, hydroids, the whole shoreline community—were buried in oil. It took only a few days to wipe out a sphere of life that had existed since before the time of mankind. Then the wind changed, and the floating slicks were carried across the English Channel to the coasts of France, where the whole grim story was repeated. Attempts to contain the oil or to remove it by chemical means were unsuccessful. The *Torrey Canyon* went on gushing oil—more than 30,000 tons of it altogether—until the remaining oil was sent to the bottom when the ship was bombed at the end of March. The golden sands of Cornwall and the pink granite of the Brittany coast bore the greasy stains of the disaster for many months, and all nature's resilience was needed to restock the stricken shores with life.

Nearly 200 tankers the size of the *Torrey Canyon* are now in service, and hundreds more are being built, some of them three times as large as that unhappy vessel. How many of them will be wrecked at sea? What will happen to our coasts if one of the supertankers were to pour forth eight or ten times as much oil as the *Torrey Canyon* released? During the 1960s, the 488 American tankers of 30,000 tons or more were involved in 533 collisions. In 43 of these, oil spillage occurred. As the maritime transport of oil increases, the fouling of shores and tide pools by drifting slicks will become a commonplace event. Let barnacles and crabs beware: the automobiles and factories of the industrialized world must have fuel!

Disasters of the *Torrey Canyon* sort are not required to cause this kind of pollution. Every day, thousands of ships routinely stain the sea with oily wastes. When an oil tanker has discharged its cargo, it must add weight of some other kind to remain stable; this is usually done by filling some of the ship's storage tanks with seawater. Before it can take on a new load of oil, the tanker must flush this watery ballast from its tanks; and as the water is pumped out, it takes

A California sea lion and murre avoid oil infested waters on pain of death. Millions of other creatures, caught unawares by the gargantuan Santa Barbara oil spill, were not so lucky.

with it the oily scum that had remained in the tanks when the last cargo was unloaded. Until 1964, each such flushing of an average 40,000-ton tanker sent 83 tons of oil into the sea. Improved flushing procedures have cut the usual oil discharge to about three tons. But there are so many tankers afloat—more than 4,000 of them—that they nevertheless release several million tons of oil a year in this fashion. The

44,000 passenger, cargo, military, and pleasure ships now in service add an equal amount of pollution by flushing oily wastes from their bilges. All told, man may be putting as much as ten million tons of oil a year into the sea, according to one scientific estimate. When the explorer Thor Heyerdahl made a 3200-mile voyage from North Africa to the West Indies in a boat of papyrus reeds in the summer of 1970, he saw "a continuous stretch of at least 1,400 miles of open Atlantic polluted by floating lumps of solidified, asphalt-like oil." French oceanographer Jacques-Yves Cousteau estimates that 40 percent of the world's sea life has disappeared in the present century. The beaches near Boston Harbor have an average oil accumulation of 21.8 pounds of oil per mile, a figure that climbs to 1750 pounds per mile on one stretch on Cape Cod. The Scientific Center of Monaco reports, "On the Mediterranean seaboard practically all the beaches are soiled by the petroleum refineries, and the sea bottom, which serves as a food reserve for marine fauna, is rendered barren by the same factors."

The increasingly common practice of drilling for oil in offshore waters adds a terrible new hazard. Since oil is contained in the earth under great pressure, oil wells frequently go out of control—and regaining control over an underwater well is no simple task. In January, 1969, a well being drilled in the Santa Barbara Channel off the coast of southern California blew out. The mishap sent oil rushing up from the depths at a rate that the oil company estimated at 20,000 gallons a day for the first ten days, and which independent researchers say may actually have reached 220,000 gallons a day. While attempts to cap the runaway well dragged on for weeks without success, a slick that eventually contained millions of gallons came to foul 800 square miles of the Pacific. The lovely beaches in and around Santa Barbara disappeared under a thick coating of oil. Blobs of oil stained the shore hundreds of miles from the scene of the blowout. Massive efforts finally reduced the size of the sea-floor oil leak—but at what a cost to animal life! Kenneth P. Cantor, a Californian expert on environmental affairs, visited Santa Barbara a few

105

weeks after the catastrophe and saw this:

"Oil, oil on birds. Oil on docks. Oil on boats. Oil on beaches. No open flames or smoking in the harbor area. A stench extending for miles. Thousands of bales of hay spread over the water and on beaches to absorb oil. A sunny week-end day. No one using boats. Black death in the intertidal zone. A new kind of plague. Along the docks and piers, salesmen for every chemical company peddling the latest in oil-dispersing agents. Some give demonstrations. Getting pretty dirty! Union Oil's bird 'rescue' station at Carpenteria State Beach—a few miles down the coast. Butter is shoved down avian gullets to cleanse digestive tracts of oil. Oil, along with natural waterproofing waxes, being washed with detergents from the feathers of gulls, cormorants, western grebes, many other species. Dying birds. A dead bird is carried off in a plastic bag. . . . Birds are now no longer waterproof. Must be kept until they moult and have new, waxy feathers. Most die. . . . Oil is still being pumped from the platforms in Santa Barbara Channel. Put that in your gas tank and burn it!"

Five months later, in the summer of 1969, I explored tide pools at Newport Beach, south of Los Angeles, far down the coast from Santa Barbara. Black tongues of oil from the blowout had reached this lovely stretch of shore and the stains could still be seen. Ugly black blobs clung to an outcropping of dead barnacles. In one pool anemones had retreated to a far corner to escape the clumps of oil that had intruded on their regular habitat. One had to walk carefully to avoid smearing oneself with oil. In many other parts of the world today the oceans and the shores are dying—killed by oil. Perhaps the worst pollution problem is to be found in Italy, which until recently has paid practically no heed to ecological perils in the course of its transformation from an agricultural nation to the world's eighth or ninth most important industrial power. Some forty big oil refineries on Italy's shores pour forth waste products almost uncontrolledly. As a result, of Italy's 5,000 miles of coastline, only about 300 miles are considered unpolluted. According to Professor Carlo Mortarino of Turin University, "Our coastal

When Thor Heyerdahl tried to re-create pre-industrial exploring conditions the illusion was soon shattered as ugly blobs of oil dirtied his papyrus sailing vessel for nearly one half of his 3200 mile voyage.

waters are already dead as a source of food as an amenity. Nobody with any sense would eat shellfish in Italy, and seventy percent of our beaches are a health hazard. It is not a question of *when* the sea will be dead; for the Italian it has already happened. In other countries bordering the Mediterranean it is only a matter of time."

And if pollution of one kind or another does not entirely destroy the life of the shore, self-styled "nature lovers" may finish the job. Perhaps books like this one, which encourage people to visit the rocky coast and look for tide pools, should

107

no longer be published; for we do not merely look, we tend to take away. Every weekend hapless creatures of the shore are collected and carried off in gaily colored plastic pails—"death buckets," one marine biologist calls them. Starfish, anemones, sea urchins, and other unusual organisms seem irresistible to collectors. But within a few hours the collected animals, torn from their natural environment, have perished.

The amateur enthusiast, scooping up the most easily removed tide-pool creatures, does only some of the damage. Just as devastating are the students, supposedly being trained as scientists, who descend on beaches by the busload to gather specimens for study. They rip off barnacles and mussels, pry limpets and chitons up with knives, pull sponges and anemones from their places of refuge. In quest of the more timid species they turn rocks over, thereby exposing sheltered communities of small organisms to sun and waves. To drive out the octopuses, shrimps, brittle stars, worms, and other creatures that live in inaccessible crevices and hollows, they use squirt guns filled with chemicals that stun or paralyze larger life-forms and kill smaller ones. Dr. Gilbert Bane of the University of California, a marine biologist much concerned with the deterioration of the tide-pool zone, once watched a college science class using these methods at the shore. Afterward, Dr. Bane and his own students took a census of the animals killed and left behind by the marauding scholars. They counted these casualties: 1,175 purple sea urchins, 118 common starfishes, 21 shrimp, 16 octopuses, 8 sea bats, 8 red sea urchins, 4 crabs, 49 fish. Slain for the sake of knowledge!

Then there are the professional collectors—those who gather up starfish to be dried and sold as curios, those who seek colorful shells with high market-value, those who gather specimens for resale to research laboratories. Some of these collectors are conscientious and careful, for they are aware that they can put themselves out of work by overharvesting the shore and destroying its life. Others are concerned only with the maximum cash return for the shortest outlay of time, and casually poison entire tide pools so they can collect two or three desirable specimens. Just a few of this sort can turn a shore into a desert in a single summer.

In California, where the ransacking and looting of tide pools has been heaviest because of the high population of the coastal areas, a recent sharp drop in shore life has aroused alarm among conservationists. Large areas have been almost entirely depleted, and others that once teemed with life now offer only occasional barnacles or anemones where dozens of species formerly could be seen. Studies showed that indiscriminate collecting by the public, rather than the effects of pollution, was chiefly to blame. Now, on many beaches of the California coast, signs announce that removal of maritime organisms is forbidden by law. Passing laws is easier than enforcing them, however, and every afternoon armies of children go home from these "protected" shores carrying plastic pails that hold small prisoners certain to be dead by nightfall.

Nature's powers of replenishment are immense and, wherever local conservation laws have been enforced, the tide pools have been able to return, within a year or two, to something like their original state. In some areas a volunteer corps of citizens helps insure that the marine life remains undisturbed. But the population of California and other coastal states continues to grow. The human pressure on the environment increases ominously from year to year. The same number of tide pools face an ever-larger number of visitors, and among them are always some who come equipped with buckets, nets, jars, and the other apparatus of the collector. A hermit crab here, a few periwinkles there—and our tide pools are nibbled into desolation. Can they survive the unchecked growth of man's population? Will the tide pools remain as they have been, fascinating pocket universes, windows into the mysterious and alien world of the sea? Or will we humans find ourselves, in thirty or fifty or seventy years, alone on our planet in all our billions, deprived of the diversity of species we now still have? The choice is ours, but we must make it now.

For Further Reading

Amos, William H. *The Life of the Seashore.* New York, McGraw-Hill, 1966. An excellent text and superb color photographs.

Buchsbaum, Ralph. *Animals Without Backbones.* Chicago, University of Chicago Press, rev. ed., 1948. After many years, still the best general introduction to the invertebrates. Photographs and scores of useful drawings.

Carrington, Richard. *A Biography of the Sea.* London, Chatto & Windus, 1960. A good general introduction to the entire marine world.

Carson, Rachel. *The Edge of the Sea.* Boston, Houghton Mifflin, 1955. Lyrical and detailed description of the shore environment by a scientist who was also a magnificently poetic writer.

Cowen, Robert C. *Frontiers of the Sea: The Story of Oceanographic Exploration.* New York, Doubleday, 1969. Tides, currents, ecology, undersea geography, all explained effortlessly and well.

Cromie, William J. *The Living World of the Sea.* New Jersey, Prentice-Hall, 1966. Another general account of sea life, with good illustrations.

Deacon, G.E.R., editor. *Seas, Maps, and Men.* New York, Doubleday, 1962. A large, comprehensive survey of all aspects of man's relation to the sea, useful and informative.

**THE
WORLD
WITHIN
THE
TIDE POOL**

Farb, Peter. *Ecology*. New York, Time Inc., 1963. A clear and well-told view of the all-encompassing web of life, with dazzling color photographs.

Hay, John, and Farb, Peter. *The Atlantic Shore: Human and Natural History from Long Island to Labrador*. New York, Harper & Row, 1966. A quiet but thorough description of the ecology of an entire coastal region.

Marx, Wesley. *The Frail Ocean*. New York, Coward-McCann, 1970. A sobering and chilling report on the injuries man has done to the marine environment.

Nilsson, Lennart, and Jägersten, Gösta. *Life in the Sea*. New York, Basic Books, 1964. Notable for a phenomenal series of close-up photographs of minute sea organisms.

Silverberg, Robert. *The World of Coral*. New York, Meredith Press, 1965. Description of the coastal life of the tropics, with photographs.

—— *The World of the Ocean Depths*. New York, Meredith Press, 1968. The sea in general, with emphasis on deep-water life.

Zim, Herbert S., and Ingle, Lester. *Seashores*. New York, Golden Press, 1955. A handy illustrated guide to the plants and animals of the shore.

Index

Index

115